Old time is still a-flying

Find this same flower that smiles to-day

Gather ye rosebuds while ye may

To morrow will be dying

Folian Cheush

EX LIBRIS

GLOBAL WARMING
A Very Peculiar History

With NO added CO_2

"Climate change is the most severe
problem that we are facing today,
more serious even than the
threat of terrorism."

David King,
former chief scientific advisor
to the UK government

To my daughter, Alex

IG

Editor: Jamie Pitman

Artists: Mark Bergin, Carolyn Franklin,
David Antram, Rob Walker, Ryz Hajdul

Published in Great Britain in MMX by
Book House, an imprint of
The Salariya Book Company Ltd
25 Marlborough Place, Brighton BN1 1UB
www.salariya.com
www.book-house.co.uk

HB ISBN-13: 978-1-907184-51-2
© The Salariya Book Company Ltd MMX

1 3 5 7 9 9 8 6 4 2
A CIP catalogue record for this book is available
from the British Library.
Printed and bound in Dubai.
Printed on paper from sustainable sources.

Visit our website at **www.book-house.co.uk**
or go to **www.salariya.com**
for **free** electronic versions of:
You Wouldn't Want to be an Egyptian Mummy!
You Wouldn't Want to be a Roman Gladiator!
You Wouldnt Want to Join Shackleton's Polar Expedition!
You Wouldn't Want to Sail on a 19th-Century Whaling Ship!

Global Warming
A Very Peculiar History™

With NO added CO_2

Written by
Ian Graham

Created and designed by
David Salariya

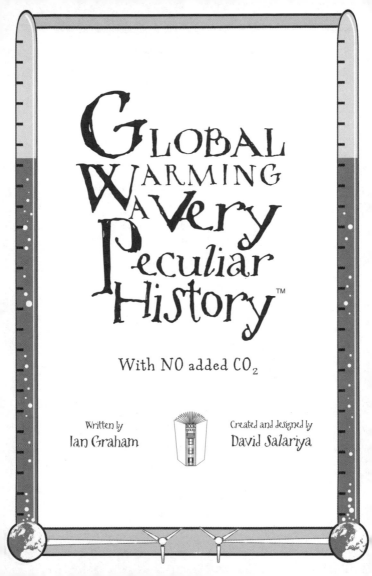

"Sea level is rising much faster and Arctic sea ice cover shrinking more rapidly than we previously expected. Unfortunately, the data now show us that we have underestimated the climate crisis in the past."

Professor Stefan Rahmstorf,
Potsdam Institute for Climate Impact Research

"Developed countries have created the problem and have a responsibility to help solve it."

Ed Milliband,
former Environment Secretary of the UK

"So today we dumped another 70 million tons of global-warming pollution into the thin shell of atmosphere surrounding our planet, as if it were an open sewer. And tomorrow we will dump a slightly larger amount, with the cumulative concentrations now trapping more and more heat from the sun."

Al Gore, former US Vice President
and environmental campaigner

Contents

The Balance of Energy

1. Solar energy passes through Earth's atmosphere and warms the ground.
2. Some energy is reflected back into space by the atmosphere.
3. Some energy is reflected back into space from the surface.
4. Earth's surface radiates some of its warmth into space.
5. The atmosphere traps some of the heat and stops it from escaping into space.

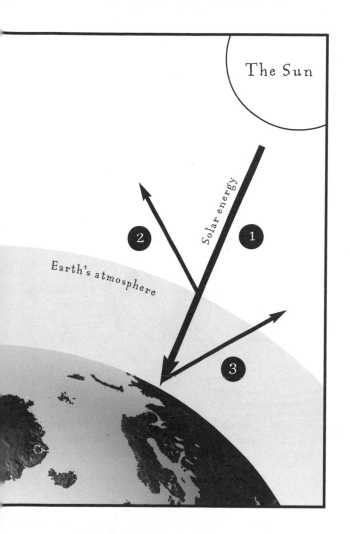

*"Now, where did I put
my sunglasses?"*

INTRODUCTION

Weather and climate are not the same. Weather is what's happening in the atmosphere in one place today and over the next few days. Climate is the average weather in one place over many years. Global climate is averaged over decades, centuries or even millennia.

It's sometimes put this way – climate is what you expect, weather is what you get.

Weather

Weather is caused by variations in temperature and moisture in different places. The Sun heats the Earth's surface, which warms the atmosphere just above it. The tropics, near the equator, are heated more than the poles, because the Sun shines more directly on the tropics than the poles. Land is heated more than ocean. Water absorbs more heat than ice. These differences in heating from place to place produce wind, cloud, rain, snow and storms – weather.

Climate

The global climate is affected by complex interactions between solar energy, the land, the sea, the atmosphere, cloud cover, ice, vegetation and, most climate scientists believe, human activities.

Earth cycles

As the Earth moves around the Sun, its tilt and its orbit changes the amount of solar energy reaching different parts of its surface. The most obvious result of this is the seasons. When one hemisphere tilts towards the Sun, it's summer there and winter in the opposite hemisphere.

The climate is affected by three natural changes called the Milankovitch cycles. They were named after a Serbian scientist and engineer, Milutin Milankovitch (1879–1958), who studied the effects of changes in the Earth's orbit on climate.

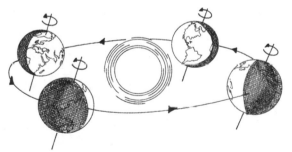

The Earth's axial tilt, spin and orbit around the sun all affect the climate.

The Milankovitch cycles are:

1. **The rotation cycle** The Earth spins like a toy spinning top, but it wobbles slightly on its axis. The wobbling is called precession. Like the other two Milankovitch cycles, the wobble changes the amount of warmth received from the Sun by the Earth, with a cycle time of 20,000 years.

2. **The tilt cycle** The Earth tilts, giving us our seasons, but the tilt changes. A greater tilt makes summers warmer and winters colder. A smaller tilt lessens the extremes of temperature. This cycle lasts 40,000 years.

3. **The orbital cycle** The Earth's orbit around the Sun expands and contracts. Sometimes the orbit is more circular and sometimes it's more flattened and elliptical. The elliptical or circular shape of the orbit is called its eccentricity. This cycle lasts 100,000 years.

Global warming

The Earth's atmosphere is a mixture of gases, mainly nitrogen and oxygen. The composition is:

Nitrogen	78%
Oxygen	21%
Other gases	1%

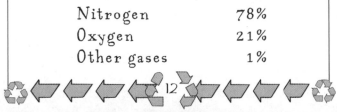

The other gases include argon, water vapour, carbon dioxide, ozone and methane.

Water vapour, carbon dioxide, methane and ozone absorb solar energy. They trap heat from the Sun. This is called the greenhouse effect and the gases that produce it are called greenhouse gases. Greenhouse gases absorb enough energy from the Sun to warm the Earth. The warming is also called global warming.

Without any greenhouse gases, the Earth would be so cold that life would be impossible. Greenhouse gases make up only 0.5% of the whole atmosphere, yet they heat the Earth to more than 30°C (48°F) warmer than it would be without them. The average temperature of the Earth is about 15°C (59°F). Without greenhouse gases, Earth's temperature would be -18°C (-0.4°F) and it would be lifeless. So, we owe our existence in part to global warming caused by greenhouse gases.

Carbon dioxide (CO_2)

Carbon dioxide represents just 0.038% of the atmosphere. It is produced in nature by respiration in plants and animals, and by erupting volcanoes. It is also produced when fossil fuels (coal, oil and natural gas) and vegetation are burned.

Water vapour (H_2O)

Water vapour is the dominant greenhouse gas on Earth. It absorbs four times more energy from sunlight than carbon dioxide. As the atmosphere warms, more water evaporates from the oceans, increasing the amount of water vapour in the atmosphere and amplifying its greenhouse effect.

Methane (CH_4)

Methane was discovered in the 1770s by Alessandro Volta, the Italian scientist who invented the electric battery. It accounts for only 0.00017% of the atmosphere, but it is 20 times more powerful than carbon dioxide as a greenhouse gas. Today, there is roughly twice as much methane in the atmosphere as there was before the industrial revolution. It comes from volcanoes, bacteria in the ground,

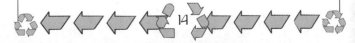

14

rubbish dumps and farm animals. It stays in the atmosphere for about 10 years before it combines with oxygen and forms carbon dioxide and water.

Ozone (O_3)

Ozone is a form of oxygen, but with three atoms per molecule instead of the usual two. It was discovered by Christian Friedrich Schönbein in 1840. Ozone in the upper atmosphere forms a life-saving layer that protects us from harmful solar radiation.

In the 1980s, scientists discovered that the ozone layer was being damaged by chemicals called chlorofluorocarbons (CFCs), which were used in fridges, air conditioners and aerosol sprays. The ozone layer was thinning, especially over the Earth's poles. The thinning was so serious that CFCs were outlawed. The ozone layer should repair itself within the next 50 years. Ozone is a greenhouse gas, but it absorbs only about a quarter of the solar energy absorbed by carbon dioxide.

A warmer Earth

Today, most climate scientists think the world is getting warmer, but not because of its tilt, spin or orbit, and not because of natural greenhouse gases either. They think it is warming up because people are adding a lot more greenhouse gases to the atmosphere.

Do you produce greenhouse gases?
Anything you do that involves burning fuel produces carbon dioxide. Since most countries generate most of their electricity in power stations that burn coal or natural gas, activities that use electricity also produce carbon dioxide. Rubbish rotting in landfill sites gives out another greenhouse gas – methane. So, if you …

Watch television	Boil a kettle
Turn on lights	Play a video game
Use a computer	Use a washing machine
Use central heating	Use a dishwasher
Use air conditioning	Vacuum the carpet
Microwave a meal	Put out rubbish

… you are probably responsible for producing greenhouse gases.

FACT BOX

Humans add about **30 billion tonnes** of carbon dioxide to the atmosphere every year, or about **4.4 tonnes** of carbon dioxide for every man, woman and child on Earth. By 2030, it could be as high as **47 gigatonnes** a year.

One kilogram of carbon dioxide would fill a large family fridge, and **1 tonne** of carbon dioxide would fill a family home.

fossil fuels

Coal, oil and natural gas are called fossil fuels, because they formed from the remains of plants and animals that lived millions of years ago.

Coal

Coal formed on land from plants that grew and died in swampy, waterlogged ground up to about 300 million years ago. First, the dead vegetation formed peat. Then the peat became buried by thick, heavy layers of mud and sediment. It sank deeper and deeper, pushed down by the weight of the layers above. The heat and pressure changed the peat into lignite (brown coal) and then black coal, a process called coalification.

Oil and gas

Oil and gas formed from plankton (microscopic plants and animals) that died in ancient oceans and sank to the bottom. To form oil and gas, the plankton had to be buried quickly by sediment before it could decay or be eaten. Heat and pressure began its transformation into oil and gas.

A temperature of 50°C (122°F) and a pressure of 250 times the pressure at the surface transformed the organic remains into a substance called kerogen. If the kerogen layers were pushed deeper, to a depth of 4000–5000 metres, by the weight of rock above them and the temperature reached 100°C (212°F), the extra heat and pressure converted the kerogen into oil and gas. Organic material containing mostly animal remains produced more oil and organic material made mostly from plants produced more gas.

Sea coal

Coal was burned as a fuel from about 5,000 years ago. It was mainly collected from natural outcrops on land, where coal seams came up to the surface, or from beaches, where the tide washed it up from coal seams that had been uncovered by the sea. Coal found on beaches is also called seacoal.

Most of the coal found on the ground and beaches, and dug out of shallow pits, had been collected and used by about the thirteenth century. After that, deeper mines had to be dug to reach coal seams further and further underground.

In the early 1800s, about 10 million tonnes of coal was mined annually in Britain. Coal production grew rapidly to meet the fuel needs of steam engines. In the early 1900s, coal production had grown to more than 250 million tonnes a year.

Ancient Oil Wells

The first oil wells were drilled in China more than 1,500 years ago. A bamboo pole with a cutting blade at the end was driven down into the ground until the oil oozed up through the hollow pole. The oil was burned to evaporate water from brine (salty water) to make salt. Gas escaping from oil-fields was burned for heat and light too.

The first modern commercial oil well was drilled in Poland in 1853. The first US oil well followed in 1859. It was drilled at Titusville, Pennsylvania, by Edwin Drake. Small amounts of oil had already seeped to the surface and people were aware that it could be used for lighting and lubrication, but no-one knew how to bring it up from under the ground. The oil that seeped to the surface was sometimes collected by a method begun by the local Seneca Indians. They placed a blanket on the ground to soak up the oil and then wrung out the blanket to obtain the oil.

Drake decided to drill down through the ground to reach the oil. Together with a local blacksmith called William A. "Uncle Billy" Smith, he built a steam-powered drilling machine. At a depth of about 20 metres (66 feet), the drill struck oil.

Who discovered global warming?

In 1861, Irish physicist John Tyndall showed that carbon dioxide gas can absorb infrared energy and warm up. And he realised what it meant. He said:

"The solar heat possesses ... the power of crossing an atmosphere. But when the heat is absorbed by the planet, it is so changed in quality that the rays emanating from the planet cannot get with the same freedom back into space. Thus the atmosphere admits of the entrance of the solar heat, but checks its exit. The result is a tendency to accumulate heat at the surface of the planet."

... or, to put it another way, the atmosphere absorbs solar energy and warms up.

Human activities

In 1896, the Swedish physicist Svante Arrhenius made the link between human activities and a man-made greenhouse effect. He wondered if the carbon dioxide produced by burning coal in industry might warm the Earth. If it did warm the Earth, he thought a warmer climate would be a good thing.

Gas trap

Since the Industrial Revolution began in Britain in the 18th century, people and industries have been pumping more and more carbon dioxide and other greenhouse gases into the atmosphere. As a result, the atmosphere traps more heat now than it did before the Industrial Revolution.

Victorian gas

The Industrial Revolution really got going in the 19th century when Queen Victoria was on the throne. Lots of industries changed from wind and water power to steam engines fuelled by coal. When coal burns, the carbon it contains combines with oxygen in the air to produce carbon dioxide... and a lot of smoke. The Victorians weren't very 'green' at all, as they:

- Burned coal at home for heat
- Burned gas at home for light
- Burned gas in street lights
- Burned coal in steam engines
- Burned coal to produce iron

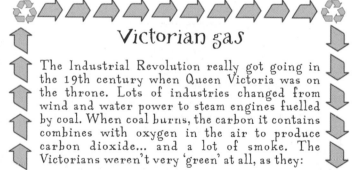

Choking smog

The Victorians burned so much coal and gas that the air in big towns and cities was full of choking smoke that blackened buildings. When it mixed with fog, it produced a deadly mixture called smog. Smogs killed thousands of people. The smogs in Victorian London were so bad that they were known as 'London Particulars' or 'pea-soupers'. Smogs continued in Britain until the 1950s, when the Clean Air Act forced people to change from coal to smokeless fuels.

FACT BOX

The Great smog of 1952 was the worst smog in London's history. It lasted **four days** (September 5-9). Between 4,000 and 12,000 people died and **100,000** suffered breathing problems.

London became known as **'The Big Smoke'** because of the black smoke pouring from its chimneys.

The curious case of the peppered moth

The peppered moth was a pale speckled moth that rested on trees. The pale colour camouflaged them so that the birds that hunted them couldn't see them. The soot and smoke belched out by chimneys and steam engines during the industrial revolution turned tree trunks black. The pale moths were easy to see and were eaten by birds. Some of the moths were darker and they survived in greater and greater numbers. The species changed colour. Then, in the middle of the 20th century, cleaner air in towns and cities led to cleaner, paler tree trunks. The darker moths were now easy for birds to find. The moth responded by changing colour again.

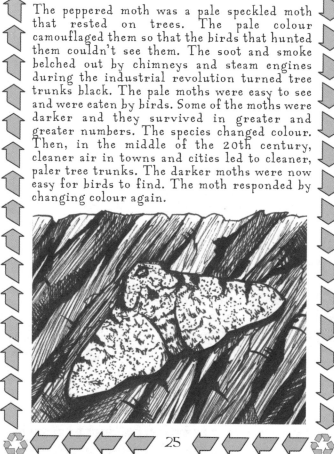

Windy cows

Agriculture produces two greenhouse gases – nitrous oxide and methane in great quantities. Nitrous oxide comes from fertilisers and methane comes from animal burps and flatulence. About 80 million tonnes of methane is released into the atmosphere by farm livestock every year. It could be as much as 128 million tonnes by 2030. That's a lot of burps!

About 90% of New Zealand's methane emissions are produced by its 45 million sheep and 10 million cattle. Researchers in New Zealand have mapped the genetic code of the microbes that live in the animals' stomachs. They are developing a vaccine that would reduce the amount of gas emitted by farm animals.

Some cows produce less gas than others. These 'low emitters' are being used as breeding stock to breed more cows that produce less gas. Another solution would be to cut the size of sheep and cattle herds, but farmers say this doesn't make sense at a time when growing populations need more food.

Earth's climate in the past

Climate change isn't a new phenomenon. It has happened many times in the past. The Earth's temperature has risen and fallen, ice has advanced across the continents and retreated again, and the sea levels have gone up and down.

About 70 million years ago, the global average temperature was 5°C (9°F) higher than it is today. At the poles, the temperature varied from 10°C (50°F) to 20°C (68°F). There was no ice at the poles. As a result, sea levels were 100 metres (330 ft) higher than they are now.

About 18,000 years ago, the world was a much colder place. In the grip of the last ice age, the global average temperature was -6°C (21°F). Nearly a third of the Earth's surface was covered with ice. Ice sheets up to 4 km (2.5 miles) thick spread out in all directions from the poles. Ice covered most of North America and Europe. With so much water locked up in ice, sea levels were 120 metres (393 ft) lower than today. The last ice age ended just over 10,000 years ago.

The Little Ice Age

Since the last ice age ended, the ice has retreated back towards the poles. Since then, the temperature has risen, but not steadily. There have been warmer periods and colder periods. One of the cold periods was cold enough to be nicknamed 'The Little Ice Age'. It lasted from the 14th century to the 19th century. The winters in Europe and North America were so cold that:

- The River Thames in London froze 26 times.
- Canals in The Netherlands froze.
- Glaciers in the Swiss Alps advanced.
- The Baltic Sea froze.
- Swedish troops were able to march across the frozen sea to Denmark in 1658 and invade Copenhagen.
- New York Harbour froze in 1780.

The River Thames in London froze many times during the Little Ice Age. At that time, the Thames was wider and shallower than it is today. It flowed more slowly, allowing ice to form more easily. King Henry VIII is said to have travelled along the frozen river by sleigh in 1536 and Queen Elizabeth I walked along the ice in 1564.

frost fairs

The Thames often stayed frozen long enough for frost fairs to be held on the ice. The first frost fair was held in 1608. Thousands of people came down to the river and went out onto the ice. They skated, cooked meals, watched plays, played games, danced and generally had a good time. There were merry-go-rounds and swings too. Stall-holders seized the opportunity to raise their prices for souvenirs.

A rhyme at the time said,

> **"What you can buy for**
> **threepence on the shore,**
> **Will cost you fourpence on**
> **the Thames, or more."**

During the Great Frost Fair of 1683–4, the ice was measured at 28 cm (11 in) thick. During the last frost fair in 1814, an elephant was taken for a walk across the frozen river at Blackfriars Bridge! After that, a warming climate and the rebuilding of London Bridge with wider arches that let the river flow faster brought the Thames frost fairs to an end.

CHAPTER ONE

ISN'T WARMER BETTER?

A warmer climate doesn't sound that bad, especially to people shivering in cold northern countries. A warmer climate in these cold countries would:

- Make farming more productive.
- Enable people to keep warm using less fuel.
- Cause fewer deaths due to freezing temperatures.
- Open up new sea routes to the north of Canada and Russia.
- Delay the next ice age.
- Boost sales of hats, shorts, sun cream and cool sunglasses.

Despite these advantages, warmer isn't better after all. As well as higher temperatures, the

effects of global warming include more frequent hurricanes, storms, floods and droughts, plus a rise in sea level, disappearing glaciers and no ice at the North Pole.

Sea level

Until the end of 2009, scientists thought that sea levels could rise by up to 90 centimetres (3 feet) by the end of the 21st century. It doesn't sound much, but many of the world's major cities are located in low-lying coastal areas. They were often founded at the mouths of rivers. A sea-level rise of 90 cm (3 ft), together with more frequent storm surges (seawater blown onto the land by strong winds), could flood these coastal areas. Some of the world's biggest cities could become uninhabitable.

Sea level rise is especially dangerous for low-lying countries like The Netherlands and Bangladesh. More than a quarter of the Dutch land area and 60% of its population are already below sea level. Most of Bangladesh is

less than 12 metres (39.4 ft) above sea level. A sea level rise of just 1 metre (3.3 ft) would flood half of Bangladesh.

In December 2009, scientists announced that they think sea levels are likely to rise faster than their earlier estimates. They now think sea levels could rise by up to 1.4 metres (4.6 ft), not 90 cm (3 ft), by 2100.

Agriculture

Higher temperatures will make crops like rice, corn and wheat grow faster, but it will also reduce their fertility. A temperature rise of about 3.3°C (6°F) would reduce crop yields by up to 40%, even without the effects of greater evaporation and drier soil, which will affect the hottest parts of the world the most. Rising temperatures have already doubled the area of land experiencing very dry conditions since the 1970s.

Salt water from rising sea levels will create another problem. Salty seawater seeping into low-lying coastal land would make agriculture impossible in those areas. Salt contamination of land and groundwater is already a problem in Bangladesh.

Research in Australia shows that higher temperatures will stress farm animals more and, for example, cause cows to produce less milk. At the same time, because of population growth, millions more people will need more food and water.

Effects on wildlife

Global warming is really bad news for wildlife. Even if the global average temperature rises by only 2°C (3.6°F) by the end of century, most of the world's endangered species (25% of mammals and 12% of birds) could disappear, because they will be unable to adapt to such rapid changes.

Warmer seas support less plankton, which some whale species, e.g. the North Atlantic Right Whale, live on. Today, there are only about 300 of these whales left. Sea turtles lay their eggs on beaches, which are threatened by sea level rise. Birds that depend on vulnerable habitats, such as wetlands, are at risk too, because their habitats could dry out in some places and flood in others.

Penguins

Rising temperatures reduce the extent of sea ice, which in turn reduces the amount of algae in the water. Krill shrimp live on these algae. Less algae means less krill, which some penguin species, such as Adelie penguins, depend on.

Adelie penguins

Fish

Some of the extra carbon dioxide pumped into the atmosphere by human activities is absorbed by the oceans, but it makes the water more acidic. Scientists recently discovered that more acidic seawater makes fish incapable of detecting nearby predators. Newly hatched fish larvae rely on their sense of smell, called olfaction, to avoid predators and seek out safe places in amongst rocky outcrops.

Clownfish bred in acidified water (to match the increase in acidity expected by the year 2100) were no longer able to detect the presence of predators. If this were to happen in nature, far fewer fish would survive to breeding age. Commercial fishing stocks could crash disastrously.

Coral reefs

Coral reefs support more species per square metre than anywhere else in the oceans. About 4,000 species of fish and hundreds of species of corals live on reefs. Scientists think there may be millions of reef species still to be discovered. The brightly coloured corals that

live in shallow tropical water are colonies of millions of tiny animals called polyps, each just a millimetre or two across. They secrete calcium carbonate, which builds up over time to form the rock-like reef.

When extra carbon dioxide in the atmosphere dissolves in the oceans, it forms carbonic acid. The acid dissolves the calcium carbonate (limestone) that coral reefs are made of. Coral reefs are also at risk of 'bleaching'. Most corals contain single-celled plants called zooxanthellae. The coral gives them a safe, sheltered place to live and the zooxanthellae produce food for the coral by photosynthesis. This sort of co-operation between species is called symbiosis.

Zooxanthellae give corals their bright, vibrant colours. However, if corals become stressed, perhaps because of pollution, or a sudden increase in temperature or acidity, they may expel the zooxanthellae. The corals lose their colour as if they had been dipped in bleach. If the bleaching is temporary, reefs can recover, but if it lasts too long, the coral dies.

Polar bears

Polar bears hunt seals from ice floes. Reducing ice means that the polar bear's hunting grounds are disappearing, and so is the seals' habitat. As a result, the bears can't find enough food for their young. This drives them onto the land to look for food. There, they come into conflict with people.

In northern Canada, polar bears are already roaming into towns, attracted by the smells of cooking and bins containing food waste. Between 1979 and 1985, 88% of the polar bears sighted in Alaska were seen on the Arctic ice. By 2005, that figure had dropped to only 10%.

Polar bears look cuddly, but they are highly dangerous animals, so they have to be captured and moved far away from human settlements. They are shot with anaesthetic darts to send them to sleep, and then taken out of the area by helicopter.

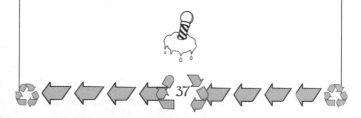

Grolar bears

Ever heard of grolar bears? Grizzly bears usually live on land. Polar bears usually live on sea ice. Normally, they don't meet, but a warmer climate enables North American grizzly bears to live further north than usual. It also melts the sea ice, forcing polar bears to move further south onto land.

The two species are now meeting and doing what bears do. The result is the grolar bear, a new hybrid bear – part grizzly, part polar bear. Its existence was confirmed by DNA analysis of a strange-looking bear shot in the Canadian Arctic in 2006.

Of all the ice floes in all the world, you had to swim up to mine...

Effects on people

Temperature

When a heat wave affected western Europe in 2003, more than 50,000 people died. Agriculture was affected too. Wheat, corn and fruit harvests fell by a third. Heat waves like this could become the norm within a century.

The hottest parts of the world today will be affected the worst, perhaps making large areas that are already difficult to survive in uninhabitable. The people who live in these places today will have to move elsewhere, probably leading to conflict and war.

Disease

Infectious diseases spread by mosquitoes and ticks will move further from the tropics into cooler regions where they do not exist today. A disease called bluetongue, which affects sheep, goats and cattle, has already started moving in this way. The virus that causes it is spread by a midge called culex imicola. Up to about 10 years ago, bluetongue was only found in Africa, because the midge could not live in the cooler countries to the north. The

warming climate since then has allowed the midge to spread out of Africa, taking the disease with it. It is now found in 12 European countries.

Diseases that infect humans will probably move and spread in the same way. Malaria is one of the biggest killers in the human population. Up to 250 million people are infected every year, and nearly a million die. In the 109 countries where malaria occurs, 3.3 billion people are at risk of infection.

By 2080, climate change will let malaria mosquitoes spread into countries that are too cool for them today. Up to 8 billion people could be at risk. Some scientists think a hotter, drier climate may kill off malaria mosquitoes in the places where they live now, so the overall number of people affected may not increase much, if at all. They will just be in different places.

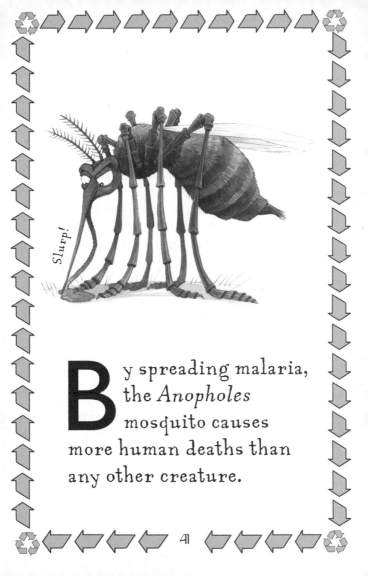

Slurp!

By spreading malaria, the *Anopholes* mosquito causes more human deaths than any other creature.

Water

Higher temperatures will make more water evaporate from the ground, robbing crops and reservoirs of precious water supplies. Rising sea levels will also pollute ground water with salt. Nearly two-thirds of the global population may be at risk of water shortage by 2025.

Australia is already experiencing severe drought conditions. Droughts have been affecting Australia since written records began in the 18th century. The latest drought began in 1995 and had not ended by the beginning of 2010, making it the continent's worst on record. As a result of this, some environmentalists believe that Australia's present rate of population growth cannot be sustained.

Food

Because of the way global warming is expected to affect agriculture, hundreds of millions more people may be affected by food shortages. Within a century, food may no longer be available from the sources that these people are getting it from now.

The US grain belt will very likely dry out. Higher temperatures will reduce rice production too. According to a study by the International Rice Research Institute, every 1°C (1.8°F) rise in the minimum night-time temperature will cut rice yields by 10%.

Weather

In a warmer world, increased evaporation from the surface will cause droughts in places. In the Sahel, the region of Africa between the Sahara and the tropical savannas to the south, rainfall has declined by 25% over the past 30 years. In other places, all the extra moisture in the atmosphere will produce more rain and heavier rain than now, causing more floods. Where there is heavier rain, there will also be more landslides, soil erosion and crop damage.

All sorts of extreme weather conditions are expected to become more common. Hurricanes can form if the ocean temperature is above 27°C (81°F). A warmer world will mean more hurricanes and worse hurricanes. Hurricane activity has been higher than average in every year since 1995 except 1997 and 2006.

CHAPTER TWO

HOW BAD WILL IT BE?

No-one really knows how bad global warming will be, because the land, oceans and atmosphere interact with each other in such an amazingly complicated way that it is difficult to predict the future. If the amount of carbon dioxide in the atmosphere continues to increase at current rates, it will have doubled compared to pre-industrial levels by 2050. Some scientists think the temperature could rise by between 1.4°C (2.5°F) and 5.8°C (10.4°F) by the end of this century. Others think the temperature rise will be smaller.

Counting the cost

The Global Humanitarian Forum, a group of government, international and business representatives founded by former United Nations Secretary General Kofi Anan in 2007, estimates that global warming already:

- Causes more than 300,000 deaths a year
- Severely affects more than 300 million people
- Places 500 million people at extreme risk
- Displaces more than 20 million people
- Causes economic losses of US$100 billion

And by 2030, they think it will:

- Cause 500,000 deaths a year
- Severely affect 650 million people
- Displace more than 75 million people
- Cause economic losses of more than US$300 billion

The cost of doing nothing to protect people and property facing these risks is potentially many times higher than spending money now. For example, the cost of providing New Orleans with greater flood protection has been dwarfed by the social and financial cost

of the damage done when Hurricane Katrina struck the city in 2005.

About 80% of New Orleans and the surrounding land was flooded. More than 1,800 people died and 700,000 were evacuated. Property damage is estimated to have cost about $100 billion. Five years on, New Orleans still had not fully recovered. And this is just one city and the effect of one storm. This could be multiplied many, many times over by global warming.

Coping with sea level rise

If the sea level is going to rise, what can we do? We could give in and evacuate people from low-lying coastal land, or we could try to protect the coast from flooding. However, coastal protection is very expensive. One estimate of the cost of protecting the US coastline from a 1-metre (3 feet) rise in sea level is US$156 billion, or about the same cost as the entire Apollo space program.

Top Ten at risk

According to a report from the OECD (Organisation for Economic Co-operation and Development), about 40 million people are at risk of a 1-in-100-year flood. By 2070, they expect this number to have more than tripled to 150 million. And the value of property and other assets at risk is expected to rise from $3 trillion today to $35 trillion by 2070.

The top ten cities most at risk from climate change by the year 2070 are:

1	Kolkata (Calcutta), India
2	Mumbai (Bombay), India
3	Dhaka, Bangladesh
4	Guangzhou Guangdong, China
5	Ho Chi Minh City, Vietnam
6	Shanghai, China
7	Bangkok, Thailand
8	Rangoon, Myanmar
9	Miami, Florida, USA
10	Hai Phong, Vietnam

If the list is redrawn to show the value of assets at risk, Miami takes the number one spot, followed by New York. If Miami were to suffer a 1-in-100-year flood, $400 billion of property would be at risk. By 2070, this is expected to rise to more than $3.5 trillion. However, the growth of Asian economies and mega-cities with huge populations mean that eight of the top ten cities at the greatest financial risk by 2070 will be in Asia.

Protecting The Netherlands

The Dutch Delta Commission predicts that the sea level around the Dutch coast will rise by up to 1.3 metres by 2100 and by up to 4 metres by 2200.

The Dutch already know what would happen if their sea defences were to fail. A storm in the North Sea in 1953 breached their sea defences and flooded the land. Nearly 2,000 people died. After that, the Dutch protected their country by building hundreds of kilometres of sea walls called dykes.

Rotterdam, the biggest port in Europe, is working to make itself climate-proof by 2025. The entrance to the port is protected by a massive structure called the Maeslant storm surge barrier. It is one of the biggest moving structures on Earth. If the port is threatened by a storm surge, a bulge of water being pushed onto the coast by a storm, the barrier can be closed to stop the port from being flooded.

Building the barrier

The Maeslant storm surge barrier is composed of two huge steel gates. Each gate is 22 m (72 ft) high and 210 m (690 ft) long. Normally, they sit out of the way in dry docks cut into the river banks. If the barrier has to be closed, shipping is given four hours' warning. With two hours to go, all shipping on the canal stops. Thirty minutes before closure, the docks are flooded. The gates are designed to float. They float out of their docks across the mouth of the Nieuwe Waterweg (New Waterway) ship canal. When they meet in the middle of the waterway, they are filled with water to make them sink. When they land on the riverbed, they seal off the port from the sea.

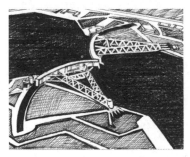

The Maeslant storm surge barrier, in Rotterdam.

Construction of the massive project was completed in 1997 at a cost of 450 million Euros. The whole structure and closure sequence is controlled automatically by a computer system that decides when to close the barrier according to weather and sea level data.

The boy who saved Holland... or did he?

There is a famous story about a boy, called Hans Brinker, who is said to have saved Holland from flooding by sticking his finger in a hole in a dyke. BUT, the story is a myth invented by an American writer, Mary Elizabeth Mapes Dodge, in 1865. So many Americans wanted to visit the place in Holland where the story was set that the Dutch Bureau of Tourism put up a statue of Hans Brinker at Spaarndam in 1950. And now there is another (miniature) statue of Brinker at a tourist attraction in Madurodam near The Hague, the Netherlands' capital city.

That sinking feeling

Britain has an extra problem in dealing with the effects of global warming. Not only is the sea level expected to rise, but part of Britain is sinking! During the last ice age, most of Britain was covered by a thick layer of ice. It was thickest in the north. It was so heavy that it weighed the land down. When the ice retreated, the land was no longer pressed down by it. Since the ice retreated, the land has been slowly rising again.

As the ice was thickest and heaviest in the north, the land has been rising most in the north. Even though the ice retreated thousands of years ago, the north of Britain is still rising today. As the north of Britain rises, the south sinks, making the effects of sea level rise there even worse.

FACT BOX

If all the mountain glaciers and icecaps were to melt, sea levels would rise by half a metre (1.6 ft), but if the largest ice sheet (the East Antarctic Ice Sheet) were to melt, the sea level would rise by a whopping **64 metres (210 ft)!**

Could warmer mean colder?

Global warming doesn't necessarily mean that temperatures everywhere on Earth will rise. Some places could actually get colder. According to one theory, it is possible that global warming could actually make the Scandinavian countries and British Isles colder. These countries are warmed by an ocean current called the North Atlantic Drift, part of the Gulf Stream that comes all the way across the Atlantic Ocean from the Gulf of Mexico. It's part of a worldwide ocean current called the thermohaline circulation (or 'great ocean conveyor'). It constantly moves water around the world.

Warm water flowing away from the tropics towards the north cools down. When it is cold enough, it becomes denser and sinks. Then it flows back towards the tropics along the bottom of the ocean and continues on its way around the world. It rises to the surface again in the Indian Ocean and Pacific Ocean. It takes about 1,600 years for the water to go all the way round the world.

If the great ocean conveyor were to stop flowing, this would cut off the supply of warmer water from the tropics and the ocean temperature in the Arctic would fall, cooling the air above it. The average temperature could drop by about 8°C (14.4°F).

The Great Ocean Conveyor

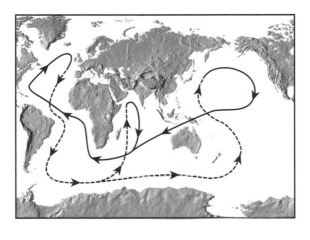

= Flow of hot water
= Flow of cold water

The strange case of global dimming

An effect called global dimming complicates global warming and it may hold a nasty surprise for the future. It seems that we've been receiving less sunlight than we thought we were getting.

The story began in Israel in the 1950s. Records of the amount of sunlight reaching the ground between then and the 1990s showed an astonishing reduction of 22% in the intensity of sunlight. The scientist who discovered this, Dr Gerry Stanhill, looked at records from elsewhere in the world and found that sunlight levels had been falling all over the world. They were down by 10% in the USA, 16% in Britain and nearly 30% in the former Soviet Union. Sunlight seemed to have been dimming by 1-2% globally per decade since the 1950s.

The dimming was caused by air pollution. Microscopic particles of soot, ash, sulphur compounds and other substances given out by industry and burning fuel were blocking some

of the sunlight. And because they attracted water droplets, they produced more clouds. This magnified the effect by reflecting even more sunlight back into space.

Then scientists realised what this meant for global warming. If the world was warming, while it was also receiving less sunlight, then global warming could be even worse without the cooling effect of the dimming. This solved a problem scientists had discovered when they compared past records with those of today.

The same rise in carbon dioxide that has produced a warming of 0.6°C (1°F) today produced a much bigger rise in temperature of 6°C (10.8°F) in the distant past. The scientists wondered if the atmosphere is less sensitive to carbon dioxide today. But the answer was global dimming, which was reducing the amount of warming. Problem solved. But this means that the atmosphere may be more sensitive to rises in carbon dioxide than scientists had thought. Not only are carbon dioxide levels rising, but the atmosphere is also becoming less polluted. The cooling effect of global dimming may not be there to help us in future.

Mass extinctions

The climate has sometimes changed quite abruptly in the past. The temperature in Greenland rose by 10°C (18°F) in a few years about 11,600 years ago. It happened at the end of a mini ice age called the Younger-Dryas Event. Further in the past, there were more catastrophic climate changes that wiped out large numbers of species. These events are called mass extinctions.

There have been five mass extinctions in the Earth's history.

- **Cretaceous-Tertiary**: 65 million years ago
- **Triassic-Jurassic**: 200 million years ago
- **Permian-Triassic**: 250 million years ago
- **Late Devonian**: 370 million years ago
- **Ordovician-Silurian**: 445 million years ago

The Permian-Triassic Extinction Event 250 million years ago was so catastrophic that up to 95% of all species were driven to extinction. It was caused by a dramatic rise in carbon dioxide that in turn caused a sudden rise in temperature. The temperature climbed until it was up to 30°C (54°F) higher than today.

Blame the Traps

Massive volcanic eruptions, called the Siberian Traps, could have been the trigger that added enough carbon dioxide to the atmosphere to cause the temperature rise. The rapid warming disrupted the normal ocean currents, which led to oxygen levels in the sea falling. This would have killed some species, but it had another effect that did even more damage. Falling oxygen levels encouraged anaerobic bacteria to flourish. Anaerobic bacteria thrive in the absence of oxygen. They produce hydrogen sulphide, which we recognise as the smell of rotten eggs. This would have killed off most of the remaining life in the ocean and spread into the atmosphere, killing plants and animals on land too. Life took about 30 million years to recover from this disaster.

Death by climate change

Scientists think that four of the five great mass extinction events may have been caused by climate change. The fifth mass extinction, when the dinosaurs died out 65 million years ago, is usually explained by the effect of an asteroid hitting the Earth. The crater left behind by the asteroid's impact was found in the 1970s on the Yucatan Peninsula in Mexico. When the asteroid hit the Earth, it would have caused earthquakes, volcanoes, fires and giant tsunami waves. In addition, all the crust material thrown up into the atmosphere would have plunged the world into darkness. This is the event that is said to have ended the rule of the dinosaurs on Earth and made way for the mammals.

It's a great story, but some scientists think the asteroid theory is wrong and even this mass extinction may have been caused by climate change.

Some of the evidence from Mexico suggests that the asteroid may have hit the Earth as much as 300,000 years before the mass extinction. It is possible that the two events are not linked at all. In one place, researchers found evidence of 52 species of creatures in the sediment immediately below the asteroid layer. All 52 species are still there in the sediment immediately above the asteroid layer. None of them were wiped out by the asteroid.

So what did happen?

At about the same time as the dinosaurs died out, huge volcanic eruptions called the Deccan Traps occurred on the Deccan Plateau in India. The lava that flowed out of them covered an area half the size of modern India. Vast quantities of sulphur dioxide would have poured out. This would have formed clouds of acid droplets in the atmosphere, producing acid rain and dimming the Sun. Less solar energy would have reached the ground and the whole Earth would have cooled. Evidence suggests that the average temperature did indeed fall.

Mass extinction 6?

Scientists also think that we may now be at the beginning of the Earth's sixth mass extinction and that it, too, is being caused by climate change. But it isn't nature alone that is driving species to extinction. This time we may be the cause.

CHAPTER THREE

HOW FAST WILL IT HAPPEN?

limate change appears to be happening faster than scientists predicted just a few years ago. Ice is melting, glaciers are retreating and the sea level is rising faster and faster.

- The Greenland and Antarctic ice sheets are melting and contributing to sea level rise at an increasing rate.

- By 2009, the area of the Arctic sea ice that melted in the summer was 40% greater than was predicted as recently as 2007.

- Sea level rise over the 15 years before 2009 was 80% worse than predicted.

However fast global warming happens, it is unlikely to happen as fast as shown in the film *The Day After Tomorrow*. This blockbuster movie showed the global climate switching from the climate we have today to an ice age in the space of just a few weeks. Although the weather in one spot can change dramatically within an hour or two, the onset of an ice age shown in the film would require changes in ocean currents which would probably take decades at the very least. When climate scientists talk about sudden or abrupt climate change, they're usually talking about something that takes decades, not weeks.

Super-fast global cooling was not quite what Larry had in mind when he decided it was time to cool down.

flip-flop climate

Some scientists think the climate will not continue to change gradually over a long period of time. They think it could reach a tipping point and then change rapidly, like a roller coaster car reaching the top of a hill and then suddenly accelerating down the other side. Scientists have found evidence that this has happened in the past. A sudden change in climate a million years ago doesn't appear to be linked to any of the natural cycles of climate change that were operating at that time. Until a million years ago, the Earth plunged into an ice age every 40,000 years. Then this regular planetary climate clock suddenly switched to a 100,000 year gap between ice ages. Yet nothing changed in the Earth's orbit to make this coming and going of ice ages change.

Now, scientists think the climate itself may have caused the change. Scientists from the Niels Bohr Institute in Copenhagen, Denmark, studied the layers of sediment in the seabed, which contained clues to the climate in the past. A million years ago, the

atmosphere may have had the lowest ever level of carbon dioxide. With so little of this greenhouse gas to trap solar energy and warm the atmosphere, the Earth cooled. It cooled and cooled until it reached a tipping point, when it switched abruptly to a different rhythm of ice ages and warm periods.

Why bother?

Why bother spending effort, time and money trying to understand what happened a million years ago? If scientists can understand what made climate patterns change suddenly in the past, it may enable them to predict future climate change with more confidence. If falling carbon dioxide levels caused abrupt climate change in the past, the question is – could rising carbon dioxide levels today cause a sudden climate change in our time?

Scientists are searching for one million year old ice in Antarctica that may contain traces of the Earth's atmosphere from that time. If they could find it, analysing it might confirm whether low carbon dioxide levels did indeed push the climate over the edge a million years ago.

Robotic scalpel

Although a 'sudden' change in climate would probably take decades, Canadian researchers think they may have found evidence that it did indeed happen much faster than this at least once in the past. Luckily for us, the conditions that caused it don't exist today. The scientists used a very precise robotic scalpel to cut thin slices just 0.5-1 mm thick from mud brought up from the bottom of Lough Monreagh, a lake in western Ireland. Each slice represents no more than three months of sediment deposited on the lake bed 12,800 years ago.

Analysing carbon isotopes (different forms of carbon) in each sample revealed how much life there was in the lake. Analysing oxygen isotopes revealed changes in the temperature and rainfall. The results suggest that the lake's temperature fell so fast that it was lifeless within a few months. The temperature went on falling for another year or so. If these astonishing findings are correct, it took less than two years for a mini ice age to take hold. The researchers think they know why it happened: a 'mega flood'.

Mega flood

About 12,800 years ago, there was a great lake covering present-day Manitoba in Canada. It held as much water as all of North America's great lakes combined. When it burst its banks and flooded out into the ocean, the sudden addition of so much fresh water made the ocean less salty. This made it impossible for the water to become dense enough to sink. As this sinking drove ocean currents in the North Atlantic and Arctic, these currents turned off. Their warming effect on the atmosphere above them turned off too and the temperature plummeted.

Fortunately, we are not threatened by a vast lake in North America bursting its banks. The Arctic ice is melting and adding fresh water to the ocean, but not fast enough to turn off the ocean currents that warm the region. However, scientists have discovered a hidden danger underneath the oceans that have the capacity to trigger a runaway greenhouse effect – methane hydrates.

Hidden danger

The greatest danger to the climate today may be hidden under the ground and in the ocean floor. Methane is a powerful greenhouse gas. Its greenhouse effect is more than 20 times more powerful than carbon dioxide's. A sudden release of large amounts of methane into the atmosphere could trigger a sudden episode of rapid warming. Unfortunately, there is a vast store of methane sitting underground, like a ticking time-bomb, and global warming could release it.

There are deposits of methane, called methane clathrates or methane hydrates, in permafrost and at the bottom of the ocean. They formed during the last ice age. Methane hydrate looks like ordinary ice or snow until it warms up. Ice and snow simply melt as they warm, but methane hydrate pops and fizzes as methane gas escapes from it. Methane is flammable. Striking a match near a chunk of warming methane hydrate sets it on fire, giving it its other name – fire ice.

The amount of methane locked up in the ground is estimated to be 3,000 times the amount of methane currently in the atmosphere. If higher temperatures caused by global warming were to melt the methane hydrate deposits, billions of tonnes of methane could be added to the atmosphere – oops!

In the 1970s, methane hydrates were treated as an amusing novelty – ice that burns. But since their potential for wrecking the climate was realised, they're being taken a whole lot more seriously.

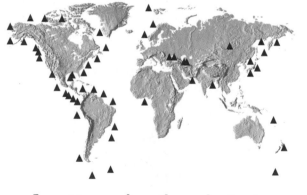

Locations of methane hydrates around the world

The climate gun

Methane hydrates are kept frozen and locked up in the ground where they are under pressure and cold, but if they warm up, they thaw out and release methane into the atmosphere. This is already happening in the Siberian Arctic, where the ice is retreating and the permafrost is melting. In 2008, scientists who sailed along Russia's north coast found methane levels in the atmosphere 100 times higher than normal. In places, they saw the sea foaming with gas bubbling up from the seabed. Scientists think this may be happening because the permafrost on land is thawing out, sending warmer water down Siberia's rivers into the sea and raising the sea temperature. The region has experienced a warming of 4°C (7.2°F) in recent decades.

The nightmare scenario is one where global warming releases enough methane to worsen global warming, which releases more methane and so on in a run-away greenhouse effect. This is also known as the clathrate gun, because once it starts, like a gun being fired, it can't be stopped. Keep your fingers, and everything else, crossed and hope that it never happens.

New fuel?

Natural gas is mostly methane and of course we use natural gas for heating and cooking. With possibly only about 60 years of natural gas from current sources left, energy companies are eyeing methane hydrates as a source of energy for the future – if only they could work out how to get it out of the ground. One method might be to pump water down into the methane hydrate deposits, which would force the gas back up.

CHAPTER four

SHOW ME THE EVIDENCE

In 1938, British engineer Guy Stewart Callendar discovered that the amount of carbon dioxide in the atmosphere had risen 10% in the previous century and when he studied temperature statistics he found that the average temperature had risen too. He concluded that the rise in carbon dioxide had caused the rise in temperature. In 1955, Gilbert Plass proved that adding carbon dioxide to the atmosphere can indeed raise the global temperature. In 1958, Charles Keeling began monitoring carbon dioxide levels in the atmosphere. He detected an increase after only two years.

The JASON report

The 'Jasons' are a secret group of scientists who advise the US government. In 1979, they produced a report called "The Long Term Impact of Atmospheric Carbon Dioxide on Climate", which predicted the rises in carbon dioxide and temperature that we are seeing now. The report, which was never released to the public, worried the US government. If global warming was a real and serious problem, the USA was the world's biggest emitter of greenhouse gases, so it would become the world's number one villain. And solving the problem could be very costly indeed. The government asked for another report, this time from a group of climate scientists, perhaps hoping for a different outcome. However, this report confirmed the Jasons' findings. What did the government do? It commissioned a third report!

The government requested the third report from a scientist called Bill Nierenberg, who had worked on the Manhattan Project to build the first atomic bomb. He went on to form the Climate Research Division at the Scripps Institution of Oceanography. He was also a Jason. Nierenberg's opinion was that climate change would not be a serious problem for many years, by which time science and technology might have come up with a solution, so there was no need to worry for a while. This enabled the US government to put global warming on the back burner and leave it for another day and another President.

What's happening today?

If global warming really is happening, then we should be able to see its effects – and we can.

Temperatures are rising – The average global temperature rose by about 0.7°C (1.2.°F) during the 20th century. In 1990, the 1980s were declared the hottest decade on record. They held the record until 1999, when the 1990s were declared the hottest decade. They held the record until 2009, when the first decade of the 21st century was declared the hottest decade. Can you see a pattern emerging?

Nearly all the glaciers on Earth are retreating – Glaciers have been retreating since 1850. Any rise in temperature will accelerate this, and just such an acceleration has been observed in several places, including the Andes in South America and the Alps in Europe. Even with the current rate of warming, all the glaciers in the US Glacier National Park in Montana may be gone by 2030. The glaciers on some Arctic islands are retreating at the rate of 150 metres a year.

Sea ice is disappearing – The Arctic is warming faster than anywhere else on Earth. Summer sea ice in the Arctic may disappear altogether some time between 2012 and 2030. The Antarctic is more complicated. Some parts of Antarctica are gaining ice, but other parts are losing ice. In 2008, 414 square kilometres (160 square miles) of the Wilkins Shelf, a vast Antarctic ice shelf, broke away from the Antarctic coast.

Sea levels are rising – Sea levels are monitored on the Earth's surface and from satellites in space. One of the satellites, GRACE (Gravity Recovery and Climate Experiment), measures the average sea level to the nearest millimetre (0.04 inches). The data shows that the sea level rose 15–20 cm (6–8 in) during the 20th century. Two of the Kiribati islands in the Pacific have already disappeared under water. Thailand, Israel, China and Vietnam have suffered saltwater contamination of their fresh water supplies because of sea level rise.

The Thames Barrier

The Thames Barrier was built in the early 1980s to protect London from flooding. When dangerously high seas are expected, its gates, which normally lie on the river bed, are raised into position to shut out the sea. It was closed once or twice a year in the 1980s. In the 1990s, it had to be closed four times a year on average. In 2003, it had to be closed on 14 tides in a row. Because of sea level rise, it may not be able to protect London after about 2065.

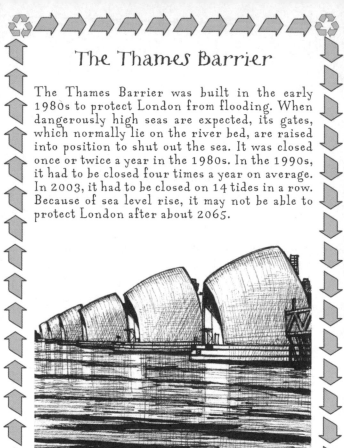

The Thames Barrier, on the River Thames in London.

The Maldives

The Maldives are a group of coral atoll islands in the Indian Ocean, southwest of Sri Lanka. There are 1,192 islands, of which 200 are inhabited by about 400,000 people.

A coral atoll forms when coral grows around a volcano in the ocean. Over millions of years, the volcano sinks back down under the water. The coral continues to grow, forming a ring-shaped reef with a lagoon in the middle.

Coral can respond to gradual changes in sea level. If the sea level falls, more of the coral is exposed, dies and is broken up by weathering. If the sea level rises, the coral grows back until it reaches the surface. However, if you're living on a coral atoll and the sea level rises faster than the coral can keep pace with, you'd better learn to swim. To make matters worse, coral is very sensitive to temperature changes, so a warming ocean may slow down coral growth or stop it altogether. This is the bind the population of the Maldives finds itself in.

The average ground level in the Maldives is only 1.5 metres (5 ft) above sea level. The highest point on the Maldives is only 2.3 metres (7.5 ft) above sea level – that's the lowest high point of any country. Any significant sea level rise could make the whole nation uninhabitable. The plight of the Maldives has been likened to that of a canary in a coal mine. Canaries were taken down coal mines because they keeled over and died at the slightest whiff of toxic gas, long before the miners were affected. If the sea level continues to rise, the disappearance of the low-lying Maldives below the waves will act as a canary warning to the rest of the world.

To highlight the urgency of the situation, the Maldives President, Mohammed Nasheed, and his government held the world's first underwater cabinet meeting in October, 2009. The politicians donned scuba gear and sat at desks on the seabed, communicating with each other by hand signals. The Maldives government is taking sea level rise so seriously that it is thinking of buying a new homeland, possibly in India, Sri Lanka or Australia, in case everyone has to leave the islands.

How do we know the Earth really is warming?

We have been measuring the temperature for only about 160 years, but there are ways of finding out how warm or cold it was thousands or even millions of years ago. We can look at:

- Written records
- Tree rings
- Fossils
- Ice cores

These 'second-hand' indicators of temperature are called proxies.

Written records

People have written down stories of floods, droughts, heat waves, bumper harvests, failed crops, ice-locked harbours and so on for most of our recorded history. Although these accounts do not provide a continuous record, they are nevertheless useful additional data.

Tree rings

Each year a tree grows and its trunk thickens by an amount that depends in part on the temperature. Trees grow more in the summer than in winter, and they generally put on more growth in a warmer summer than a cooler summer. A tree's annual spurts in growth, which appear as concentric rings of dark and light lines in the wood, represent a record of the weather. The tree ring record goes back as far as 26,000 years.

Fossils

Knowing which creatures and plants lived in a region indicates what the climate was like. This valuable information is recorded in fossils. Microscopic creatures called forams are very useful clues to ocean temperatures. The numbers of the different foram species that live in the ocean are very sensitive to changes in temperature. When they die, they sink to the seabed. Analysing foram skeletons in seabed sediments reveals the rises and falls in the ocean temperature.

Ice cores

Ice cores are cylindrical slugs of ice drilled out with a hollow drill. Each core is about 10 cm (4 inches) across. A few metres at a time are drilled out. Ice cores have been drilled down to a depth of about 3.6 km (11,800 ft). The amount of snow and ice laid down each year is clearly visible as a series of lines across the core. Bubbles in the ice trap tiny samples of the atmosphere from when the ice formed. Pollen dust and other debris blown on the ice and trapped there give more clues to the climate. Ice cores represent about 800,000 years of atmospheric records.

Storms and floods

If there are dreadful storms, floods or a heat wave this year, is this evidence of global warming? No. We have always had extreme weather events. One year with particularly bad storms, floods, droughts or other extreme weather means nothing. Despite a warming trend in the climate, one particularly cold year doesn't signal the end of global warming. The winter of 2009–2010 was the coldest and snowiest in Britain and parts of North America for several decades. Fifty years from

now, the world will probably be warmer than it is now, but there will still be unusually cold winters in places from time to time. Climate scientists take more notice of long term trends, rather than what happens in one year. They call these annual variations in weather 'noise'.

*"Global warming?
What global warming?"*

Jet streams

The jet streams are bands of strong winds that blow around the world. There are four main jet streams – a polar jet stream near each pole and a subtropical jet stream closer to the equator in each hemisphere. The polar jet streams are the fastest, blowing at 300 kph (186 mph).

The weather patterns that flow from west to east across the northern hemisphere are controlled by the polar jet stream. This is the region where warm air from the tropics meets cold air from the Arctic. Exchanges of energy between the two masses of air create storms that follow the path of the jet stream. The shape and position of the jet stream determines which countries are hit by these storms. So, if one year is particularly stormy or there are floods, it may not be anything to do with climate change. It may just be that the polar jet stream is stuck over you and dumping a series of storms in your lap. Global warming may move this jet stream further north during the Summer. The Atlantic depressions that bring rain to the British Isles and western Europe may move with it, causing drought conditions.

The 'Hockey Stick'

The 'Hockey Stick' is one of the most controversial pieces of evidence presented in climate science. It's a graph that shows how the Earth's temperature has changed over the past 1,000 years. It's called the Hockey Stick because it's the shape of a hockey stick lying on its side. Until about 1800, the graph shows the temperature remaining relatively stable and flat, like the handle of a hockey stick. Then it shoots up like a hockey stick's blade, showing the temperature rising remorselessly through the Industrial Revolution right up to the present day.

The controversy that rages about it surrounds the methods used for taking data from different sources and combining them in one graph. Information from tree rings, ice cores, lake-bed sediments, coral growth and other studies were combined to produce the hockey stick handle part of the graph. Critics say that accurate temperature records exist for only the past 160 years, so the shape of the rest of the graph can't be known as accurately.

The graph and the methods used to create it have been tested and analysed endlessly since it was published in 1998 and some researchers have produced graphs with a less flat 'handle'. In 2006, the US National Research Council investigated the Hockey Stick for Congress and reported that, although the temperature data is less reliable before 1600, the rise in temperature of the past few decades is real.

The 'Hockey Stick' Graph

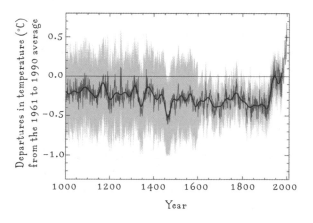

This chart is Figure 1(b) from the Intergovernmental Panel on Climate Change Third Assessment Report, (c) 2001 The Intergovernmental Panel on Climate Change.

The Spanish children

The Pacific Ocean is the largest of all the oceans. When something big happens in the Pacific, the rest of the world feels the effects. Two weather events in particular affect weather around the world. They're called El Niño and La Niña – Spanish for the little boy (or Christ child) and the little girl.

El Niño

The trade winds normally blow from east to west across the tropical part of the Pacific Ocean, from Ecuador to Indonesia. The winds blow the surface water towards the west, drawing deep cold water up to the surface off the coast of South America to replace it. This cools the air above it, stabilising the air and producing the region's dry weather. On the other side of the ocean, moisture evaporating from the warm water gives Indonesia its high rainfall. Every few years, the winds weaken or reverse. Warmer water in the western Pacific spreads eastwards across the ocean. This is an El Niño event.

El Niños stop the upwelling of cold nutrient-rich water off the South American coast, bringing a halt to fishing. The normally dry weather in Peru and Ecuador switches to rain and floods. Meanwhile, on the other side of the Pacific, the rain in Indonesia dries up. The knock-on effects continue all round the world.

Here are some facts about El Niño:

- An El Niño event happens every 2-7 years.
- It can last 1-2 years.
- Each El Niño event is usually followed by a La Niña event lasting about a year.
- The most severe El Niño occurred in 1982-3. The damage it caused, due to storms, drought, failed crops and fish catches, floods, bush fires and mudslides, is estimated to have cost more than US$8 billion.

La Niña
The opposite event to El Niño is La Niña. The upwelling of cold water in the eastern Pacific intensifies, cooling the eastern Pacific. The effects are the opposite of an El Niño. The eastern Pacific experiences drier weather and fishing improves. Rainfall increases over the western Pacific.

CHAPTER fIVE

WHO PRODUCES THE POLLUTION?

n average, every person on Earth pumped about 4.4 tonnes of carbon dioxide into the atmosphere in 2008, but some people produced a lot more than the average. Some of this extra carbon dioxide is mopped up by the oceans. Some of the rest is taken up by green vegetation, but a large chunk of it stays in the atmosphere.

The winner of the world's worst carbon dioxide emitting country title is China, with the USA coming a close second.

WHO PRODUCES THE POLLUTION?

Country	Total CO_2 emissions (million tonnes, 2006)
1. China	6018
2. USA	5903
3. Russia	1704
4. India	1293
5. Japan	1247
6. Germany	858
7. Canada	614
8. UK	586
9. South Korea	515
10. Iran	471

Developed countries emit a lot more carbon dioxide than developing countries, because people in developed countries love their cars and their power-hungry kitchen appliances, heating (or air-conditioning) and gadgets. Most energy-intensive industries are based in developed countries too. The busiest transport routes are also located within and between the most developed countries.

FACT BOX

China, the USA and the European Union together account for **more than half** of all the world's man-made carbon dioxide emissions.

What's that you say, Skippy?

China and the USA are by far the world's worst carbon dioxide emitters, but if you look at the amount of carbon dioxide emitted per person, the picture is completely different. Australians come out as the villains. Each Australian emits nearly 21 tonnes of carbon dioxide per year, compared to Americans who each emit 20 tonnes per year.

Compared to carbon dioxide emissions of 10-20 tonnes of carbon dioxide per person per year in the wealthiest and most industrialised nations, most countries in sub-Saharan Africa emit less than 1 tonne of carbon dioxide per person per year. The average person in Nepal emits only about 110 kilograms of carbon dioxide. In other words, each Australian produces as much carbon dioxide as about 190 Nepalis.

Australians emit five times more carbon dioxide per person than the average Chinese person, but China as a whole emits more than 20 times more carbon dioxide than Australia, because the Chinese population is huge compared to the number of Australians. There are more than 1.3 billion Chinese people, but the entire population of Australia numbers only 22 million, or less than three times the population of New York City.

At 1.18 billion, India's population is very close to that of China, but India's carbon dioxide emissions per person amount to only 1.1 tonnes, less than a quarter of China's. However, China and India are both fast-developing nations whose carbon dioxide emissions are certain to rise fast in the coming years.

Australia's poor record on carbon emissions is down to its addiction to coal. About 80% of Australia's electricity is generated from coal. By comparison, nearly the same percentage of France's electricity is generated by cleaner nuclear energy. To make matters worse, Australia has been less efficient at producing

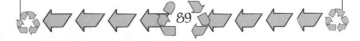

energy from coal than other countries. Australia uses up to 30% more fuel per unit of energy produced than countries such as the USA, Japan and European countries.

In addition to the coal Australia uses within its own borders, Australia also exports a lot of coal that is used elsewhere in the world. Adding it all together, Australian coal is responsible for emitting a billion tonnes of carbon dioxide every year, or more than 8% of the total global emissions from coal.

In the 25 years from 1982 to 2007, Australia's carbon dioxide emissions increased at almost twice the world's average rate. The Australian population is only 0.32% of the total global population, but it produces 1.43% of global carbon dioxide emissions.

In the 10 years from 1996 to 2006, some countries managed to cut their carbon dioxide emissions, while other countries' emissions rose dramatically. Chinese emissions more than doubled, while Poland and the Ukraine cut their emissions by 10% or more.

Where does the carbon dioxide come from?

The majority of global carbon dioxide emissions come from electricity generation, industry and transport, mainly from North America, Europe and Asia. Most of the remaining carbon dioxide emissions come from changes in land use. Most of this is caused by the clearance of forests in South America, Asia and Africa. Forests soak up a lot of carbon dioxide. When they are cut down, the carbon dioxide they would have absorbed stays in the atmosphere.

Overview of global CO_2 emissions

Transport (Road, Rail, Air & Water) **17%**

Industry **25%**

Household small consumers **9%**

Deforestation **22%**

Power/heating stations **27%**

More of the world's electricity is produced by coal-fired power stations than by any other source. Coal is the most abundant and cheapest source of energy, but it is also the dirtiest fuel. When coal is burned, carbon dioxide, sulphur dioxide, nitrogen oxides and mercury compounds are released. Methane is also released when coal is mined, cleaned and transported. Coal-fired power stations are required to reduce their emissions of these gases.

In addition to the global warming effect of carbon dioxide, sulphur dioxide and nitrogen oxides can cause acid rain. When the gases mix with moisture in the air, they form sulphuric acid and nitric acid. Acid rain kills vegetation and also fish in rivers and lakes.

Compared to cleaner nuclear power stations, you'd have to burn 800 kg (1,780 pounds) of coal to produce as much energy as you'd get from a 7-gram piece of uranium fuel the size of your finger-tip, but the nuclear fuel produces none of the pollution and greenhouse gases that the coal emits.

There are about 440 nuclear power reactors in 31 countries, but there are 600 coal-fired power stations in the USA alone. China is by far the world's biggest coal user. In 2008, China used about 3 billion tonnes of coal, or more than one third of all the coal used worldwide.

Coal facts

- Coal provided the energy that fuelled the industrial revolution.
- Coal is less than half the cost of oil or gas.
- About 38% of the world's electricity is generated from coal.
- Global oil and gas reserves are expected to last 40 and 60 years respectively, compared to about 200 years of coal.
- Coal is found on every continent from the Arctic to the Antarctic.
- Anthracite, the oldest type of coal, formed up to 400 million years ago.
- Lignite, the youngest coal, formed less than a million years ago.
- Coal was used by the Romans in Britain about 1,800 years ago.

CHAPTER SIX

ARE THE SCIENTISTS RIGHT?

Not everyone is in agreement that global warming is happening, or, even if it is, that it is caused by human activities. Scientific theories have been wrong in the past, after all.

More than 2,000 years ago, most educated people believed that the Earth was at the centre of the Universe. In the seventeenth and eighteenth centuries, scientists thought that anything capable of being burned contained a substance called phlogiston. In the early nineteenth century, infectious diseases were thought to be spread by a poisonous vapour

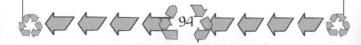

called miasma. In the early part of the twentieth century, some scientists thought that the Universe had always existed – a so-called steady state Universe. Now we know that it started about 13.7 billion years ago with the Big Bang. So could scientists be wrong about global warming today?

Dodgy scientific theories of the past

The Earth-centred Universe
More than 2,000 years ago, most educated people believed that the Earth was at the centre of the Universe. By the 16th century, some scientists who had studied the movements of the planets thought this was wrong. They

had a different idea – it was obvious to them that the Sun must be at the centre of the Universe. Their observations and calculations seemed to confirm their theory. During the 18th and 19th centuries, it became clear that the Sun was just one of many, many stars and there was no good scientific reason why the Sun should be at the centre of the Universe. Now we know that the Sun is an insignificant star in one of billions upon billions of galaxies.

Spontaneous generation

Until the late nineteenth century, it was widely believed that life could spring from non-living matter. The action of the Sun on soil and water was thought to produce simple living organisms. The winds were thought to play a part in generating life too. The Roman architect and writer Vitruvius (c 80 BC – 15 BC) believed that bookworms were produced by winds blowing from the south or west, so he said that libraries should face east. Others thought that worms and frogs arose spontaneously from mud, and maggots were produced by rotten meat. The centuries-old theory of spontaneous generation was finally disproved by experiments carried out by the French scientist, Louis Pasteur (1822–1895).

DODGY THEORY

Louis Pasteur

The miasma theory

The miasma theory held that diseases were caused by a poisonous vapour called miasma. Foul-smelling air was thought to contain miasma. Outbreaks of cholera near dirty, smelly water seemed to support the theory. Florence Nightingale (1820–1910), known as 'the lady with the lamp', is famous for her work in the military hospital at Scutari during the Crimean War. She made the wards light, airy and clean, because she believed the high rate of death was due to infectious diseases caused by bad air.

The miasma theory was finally ruled out as a cause of cholera by John Snow (1813–1858), a London doctor. When there was an outbreak of cholera in the Soho area of London in 1854, Snow thought the local water supply might be to blame. At that time, poor people got their water from hand-pumps in the street. A map of the cholera cases showed that they were close to one of these pumps. Snow persuaded the council to remove the pump handle so that people couldn't take water from the well. Cutting off the water supply brought the outbreak to an end and proved that contaminated water, not miasma, had spread the disease.

DODGY THEORY

The phlogiston theory

For more than 100 years from the 1660s, scientists explained burning by the phlogiston theory. According to this, anything that could be burned contained something called phlogiston. When it burned, the phlogiston was driven off. The problem was that when scientists were able to weigh substances accurately enough, they discovered that burning increased the weight of some substances when the theory meant that they should have lost weight.

They had expected to see the weight go down when the phlogiston was driven off. Some scientists explained the results by saying that phlogiston must have negative weight. Finally, the French scientist Antoine Lavoisier (1743–1794) proved that the phlogiston theory was wrong in 1783. He established that burning involved a chemical reaction between a substance and oxygen. Phlogiston simply didn't exist.

The aether theory

Until the 19th century, scientists thought that space could not be empty. There had to be something there for the planets, light and other radiations to travel through. They called the mysterious 'something' aether. However, not one single experiment detected any evidence for the aether. Beams of light were sent in different directions, and scientists looked for differences in the speed of the light waves caused by one beam travelling with the aether and another travelling against it. No differences were found. The final nail in the coffin of the aether theory was Einstein's special theory of relativity in 1905. It successfully described the behaviour of matter and energy in space without the need for an aether. So, another theory bit the dust.

The steady state Universe

Discoveries in astronomy in the early years of the 20th century led scientists to wonder about how the Universe began. Einstein thought the Universe had always been as it is today. It was called the static Universe. By the 1950s, most scientists agreed with the steady state Universe theory. This held that the Universe had always existed.

By then, scientists knew that the Universe was expanding. They explained this by saying that matter is constantly being created, so the Universe has no beginning and no end. The search for evidence to support this theory simply piled up more and more evidence for the competing theory – the Big Bang theory. According to this, the Universe burst out of a single point about 13.7 billion years ago and has been expanding ever since then.

Climate mistakes

The miasma and phlogiston theories and many more dodgy theories were wrong. However, none of them involved the climate. In case you're wondering if climate scientists got it wrong in the past – well, yes they have.

Hothouse or ice-house?

In the 1970s, some scientists predicted that the Earth was heading for a new ice age, because there had been a period of cooling in the middle of the 20th century. Projecting this cooling trend into the future inevitably led to an ice age. However, this was not accepted by the majority of climate scientists. Government leaders did not hold conferences to decide what to do about it. This cooling period turned out to be temporary. When warming returned and continued, it looked like an ice age was not on the way after all.

Vanishing glaciers

When the UN's climate science panel said in a report published in 2007 that most of the glaciers in the Himalayas could disappear by 2035, a number of scientists raised objections. Leading glaciologists said that such a rapid melting was not only unlikely, it was impossible. The glaciers could not melt so quickly. It was one mistake in a 3,000-page report, but it added to the objectors' suspicions about climate science data and predictions.

What do people who don't believe in the current theory of climate change say?

"Global warming isn't happening"
People who don't think global warming is real sometimes point out that 1998 was warmer than the years that followed it, so where is the evidence for global warming? 1998 was indeed warmer than the years that followed, but that doesn't mean that the atmosphere is cooling. It means that 1998 was a very hot year indeed. The trend is still upwards.

The atmosphere can sometimes cool down for a few years. Carbon dioxide is not the only factor changing the atmosphere. Sometimes, other factors temporarily balance or reverse the warming effect of carbon dioxide and the other greenhouse gases.

Lots of particles or droplets in the atmosphere can cause global cooling. In the early 1990s, there were three years of cooling, because of a huge volcanic eruption. Mount Pinatubo in the Philippines erupted in 1991. It was the second biggest volcanic eruption of the 20th century. It hurled millions of tonnes of sulphur dioxide into the atmosphere. Moisture in the atmosphere turned this into vast clouds of sulphuric acid droplets, which absorbed solar energy and stopped it reaching the surface. The global temperature dropped in 1992, 1993 and 1994. But as the effect of the volcano faded away, the greenhouse effect took over again and warming resumed.

"Global warming is happening, but it's natural, not man-made."

Some scientists have argued that global warming is real, but it is not man-made. They point to natural sources of greenhouse gases, such as volcanoes, and natural 1,500-year cycles of warming and cooling in the past million years caused by changes in solar activity.

Volcanoes - Volcanoes do produce greenhouse gas, but they produce far less greenhouse gas than humans. Human activities add 10 times more carbon to the atmosphere than volcanoes. Although volcanoes give out greenhouse gases, they also hurl so much dust and droplets into the upper atmosphere that less solar energy reaches the lower atmosphere and ground. The greenhouse gases cause warming and the dust and droplets cause cooling. Depending on how much of each is produced, volcanoes can have a warming effect or a cooling effect.

The Little Ice Age - The Little Ice Age was a cold period that occurred between about 1300 and the middle of the 19th century. We've been

warming up since then. Some people say the current warming is just a normal recovery from this cold period.

Solar activity - What about changes in solar activity? The climate experts say variations in solar activity are taken into account in climate models. But there's more to solar activity than the Sun itself. The Sun affects the number of cosmic rays reaching Earth.

Cosmic rays are particles hurtling through space at close to the speed of light. When they hit the upper atmosphere, they collide with gas atoms and produce showers of electrically charged particles called ions. These ions attract water molecules. The water droplets collect together to form clouds, which reduce the amount of solar energy reaching the ground.

The Sun has a powerful and complex magnetic field, which varies in a regular way. When the Sun is very active, its strong magnetic field stops some of the cosmic rays from reaching Earth. The Sun is thought to be more active magnetically now than at any time

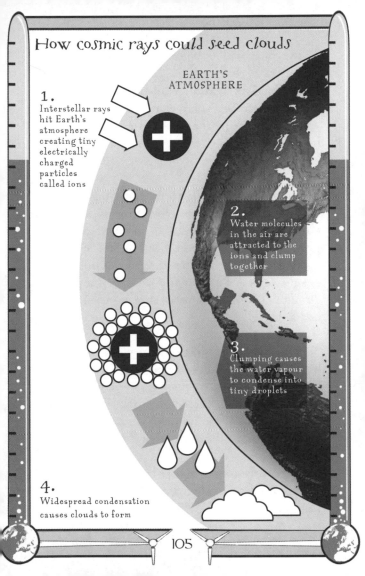

How cosmic rays could seed clouds

EARTH'S ATMOSPHERE

1.
Interstellar rays hit Earth's atmosphere creating tiny electrically charged particles called ions

2.
Water molecules in the air are attracted to the ions and clump together

3.
Clumping causes the water vapour to condense into tiny droplets

4.
Widespread condensation causes clouds to form

in the past 1,000 years, so the numbers of cosmic rays reaching the Earth is at a historic low. Cloud formation is also, therefore, very low and so more solar energy is reaching the ground, warming it and the atmosphere above it. And there, they say, you have the cause of global warming.

Scientists are divided on how big a part cosmic rays play in cloud formation and climate change. Global warming itself produces more clouds because more water evaporates from the oceans, so the impact of cosmic rays is difficult to assess. It is a part of climate science where more research is needed.

"It was warmer thousands of years ago, long before people started burning fossil fuels"
There have been warmer and colder periods throughout the Earth's history. They were mainly caused by natural variations in the Earth's orbit and solar activity.

Temperatures were higher than they are today during a period called the Holocene Climatic Optimum, about 5,000 to 9,000 years ago.

Scientists know why it was warmer. Changes in the Earth's orbit produced the higher temperatures, but only in the northern hemisphere and only in summer. The warming did not affect the whole planet as it does today.

Another warm period called the Medieval Warm Period occurred between about AD 800 to 1300. But, just like the Holocene Climatic Optimum, scientists think this was not global. The North Atlantic and parts of North America were warmer, but other parts of the world are not thought to have warmed as much. The global temperature as a whole was probably cooler during the Medieval Warm Period than it is now. Critics of this theory claim that there is not enough evidence to be sure that the Medieval Warm Period just affected the northern hemisphere.

"Global warming stopped between 1945 and 1965. Doesn't that blow a hole in man-made climate change?"
The Earth cooled by about 0.1°C between 1945 and 1965, even though industry grew rapidly after World War II. On the face of it,

it seems odd that a rapid increase in industrial activity should be accompanied by global cooling. Surely the opposite should have happened. As industrial activity accelerated after the war, emitting more carbon dioxide, shouldn't we see global warming in the record for this period?

Well, if you think about it, the cooling that happened can be explained quite easily by global dimming. The growth in industrial activity at that time was fuelled almost entirely by coal and oil. The huge amount of coal and oil that were burned produced so much smoke and droplets that the amount of solar energy reaching the ground and warming the lower atmosphere fell. In other words, the dirty atmosphere blocked sunlight. When the smoky atmosphere began to clear as a result of laws governing air pollution, global warming reappeared.

"If scientists can't forecast the weather next month accurately, how can they predict the temperature 100 years from now?"
Weather and climate are two different things. Weather forecasters assume that land, vegetation, sea, ice and solar conditions stay the same for the next few days, and only the atmosphere is changing. In climate prediction, all of these factors, and more, become variables – they all change – and all the changes have to be taken into account.

Computer models recreate the world and its atmosphere using a computer program in which the Earth's surface is divided into small squares, about 140 kilometres by 100 kilometres. The atmosphere above each square is divided into layers 100 metres thick. The computer then predicts the way the temperature, cloud, wind and other factors change over minutes, days, weeks and so on into the future.

Scientists regularly test the predictions of their computer models. They can start a model running from any date and they can run the models backwards as well as forwards. If a model can recreate the climate today, starting

from some point in the past, this shows that it is working reasonably well. And as the science of the way the atmosphere, oceans, land, ice and solar energy interact is understood better, the computer models improve too.

"The Hockey Stick is just plain wrong"
The Hockey Stick graph that has been published everywhere to demonstrate the dramatic effect of global warming has been very controversial. It has many critics. Other researchers have created their own hockey stick graphs and there are differences between them caused by the methods used, the data used and the way the data are interpreted. But most scientists agree that the steeply rising temperatures shown at the present-day end of the graph are real and still rising. But controversy rages over what the graph means for the future.

"Scientists are fiddling the data to fit their theories"
Climate scientists are often criticised for being very selective about which data they use, selecting only data that support global warming, or manipulating the raw data to make sure that they support global warming.

ARE THE SCIENTISTS RIGHT?

Raw data is indeed processed (i.e. changed) to remove abnormal or unnatural effects. One example of this is the urban heat island effect. Cities are warmer than open countryside, so temperatures collected from cities or other abnormally warm places like airports are adjusted downwards by several degrees to give the true temperature. Lots of adjustments like this are made to climate data.

Climategate - In 2009, just before an important climate conference in Copenhagen, Internet hackers obtained emails from the University of East Anglia's Climate Research Unit that, it was claimed, showed the university's climate scientists secretly suppressing or changing climate data to make it fit the man-made global warming theory. The climate scientists at the unit strenuously denied changing data to mislead anyone. Inquiries by the university itself and the House of Commons Science and Technology Committee found that there was no evidence of dishonesty or malpractice.

The University of East Anglia's Climate Research Unit is not the only organisation that collects and analyses climate data. Even without the University of East Anglia's climate research every major scientific institution dealing with the climate, ocean or atmosphere agrees that the climate is warming and the primary cause is man-made carbon dioxide emissions. If man-made global warming were to be a deliberate scam or hoax, as some people claim, it would involve the participation or co-operation of thousands of scientists all over the world, which seems unlikely.

Following publicity about the hacked emails from the University of Surrey, scientists and scientific organisations in the USA were so concerned about the effect it might have on government policy that they wrote to Congress. They said that evidence from numerous research centres all over the USA and beyond make it clear that climate change is real and that greenhouse gases emitted by human activities are the main cause.

Tim didn't realise the energy he was using to disprove man-made global warming was actually helping to make it worse.

CHAPTER SEVEN

WHAT CAN WE DO ABOUT IT?

PART 1: CUTTING GREENHOUSE GAS EMISSIONS

Although there are many ways to release greenhouse gases into the atmosphere, countries and individuals can still do a lot to reduce global warming:

- Make fossil fuels less damaging, e.g. by using carbon capture
- Develop new crops that will grow better in a warmer world
- Reduce greenhouse gas emissions from agriculture
- Reduce forest clearance
- Use more renewable energy
- Develop more environmentally friendly fuels, e.g. bio-fuels
- Increase the use of nuclear power
- Build more energy-efficient buildings

Make fossil fuels less damaging

Cutting the use of fossil fuels would certainly reduce the amount of greenhouse gases they emit. However, another way to tackle the problem is to use the fuels, but reduce or eliminate the gases they emit. Governments are trying a variety of ways to both reduce fossil fuel use and make them less damaging to the environment.

Carbon trading

Carbon trading is one of the ways that governments have tried to reduce carbon emissions. One widely used carbon trading system is called cap and trade.

Companies are given a limit for the amount of carbon they are allowed to give out. If they can't keep within the limit, they can buy carbon credits from less polluting companies. So, the most polluting businesses have to pay more and businesses that reduce their carbon emissions can make money by trading carbon credits. Carbon trading encourages businesses to reduce their carbon emissions. In 2007, US$64 billion changed hands as a result of carbon trading. Critics of carbon trading say that it does little to reduce carbon emissions. The most polluting businesses simply buy the carbon credits they need and carry on as before.

Carbon offsetting

Carbon offsetting is a system that enables people or companies to neutralise their carbon emissions. Someone who takes a long-haul flight could offset or neutralise their part of the flight's carbon emissions by paying a fee. The fee is used to invest in green projects such as renewable energy, dealing with pollution or planting trees, which would remove the carbon dioxide from the atmosphere as they grow.

Critics say carbon offsetting lets wealthy people carry on polluting instead of changing their behaviour to reduce greenhouse gas emissions. Another criticism is that if trees used for carbon offsetting might have been planted anyway, then they aren't really offsetting carbon emissions. The efficiency of forests outside the tropics as carbon offsets has been questioned. In cooler parts of the world, forests create a warming effect that balances their carbon absorption.

Once trees are paid for and planted, there is no guarantee that they will survive. In one famous example, the band Coldplay planted 10,000 mango trees in India. The aim was to offset the greenhouse gas emissions caused by the release of the band's album, A Rush of Blood to the Head, and also to support local farmers. However, many of the trees died in the dry soil due to a shortage of water.

Green taxes

Governments can use eco-taxes, or green taxes, to raise money for green policies or steer people's behaviour in a more environmentally-friendly direction. Carbon taxes make people pay more if they emit more carbon. They have been successful in reducing carbon emissions in some countries, such as Sweden and Finland, but they have failed in others, such as Norway, where carbon emissions have increased.

One problem with green taxes is that they hit the poor harder than the better off. And people are often suspicious that green taxes may be just another way for governments to raise money rather than being used to reduce greenhouse gas emissions. When the New Zealand government announced plans to impose a tax on farmers aimed at reducing gas emissions from farms, members of parliament received parcels of manure in their post!

Create new crops for a warmer world

While governments wrestle with the problem of reducing greenhouse gas emissions, it is clear to most climate scientists that the world will continue warming for some time. And at a time when the population is increasing, there is greater pressure on agriculture to produce more and more food. But the crops that farmers grow today do not do well in the higher

temperatures and droughts caused by global warming. Sub-Saharan Africa and Central Asia are particularly vulnerable to droughts. Africa has suffered seven major droughts in the past four decades. Droughts in 1972–74 and 1981–84 were particularly bad.

East Africa is affected too. Kenya's maize crop, which makes up 80% of the country's annual cereal crop, is expected to fall by perhaps a quarter because of a prolonged drought affecting East Africa. The World Food Programme has estimated that more than 20 million people in East Africa are on the brink of starvation.

One answer to Africa's food problem is to develop new strains of crop plants that are more heat-resistant and drought-tolerant. There are two ways to do this. It can be done naturally by farmers breeding plants using plants that survive drought the best. Or it can be done using biotechnology – changing a plant's genes in a laboratory. Either way, new drought-tolerant strains of rice, sorghum, millet, cassava and maize will be needed to feed Africa in a warmer world. It can take more than 20 years to develop a new strain of plant such as rice.

Crops in developed countries are being hit by drought too. In 2005, the corn crop in Spain, Portugal and France was the worst in 50 years because of drought. In 2006, corn production in the USA was down 5% due to drought.

Reduce greenhouse gas emissions in agriculture

Agriculture seems very natural and green, quite unlike all those nasty dirty engines in cars and trucks that pour out pollution. But, in fact, agriculture produces as much greenhouse gas as the whole transport sector. So, it's as important to reduce greenhouse gas emissions in agriculture as it is to clean up transport.

Burping cows – Every day, each cow pumps out 100-200 litres of methane, a powerful greenhouse gas. That's equivalent to more carbon dioxide than a 4x4 car produces in a 53-kilometre (33-mile) drive. The gas is produced as the animal digests grass.

Cows and sheep are responsible for about a quarter of all the methane produced in Britain, but some countries produce a lot more. New Zealand's farms are home to 10 million cows and 45 million sheep, which are responsible for about 90% of that country's methane emissions. Globally, about 15-20% of all methane released into the atmosphere is thought to come from animals.

The amount of methane produced by cows can be cut by feeding the cows with more easily digestible food. Rye grass with a high sugar content, white clover and bird's-foot trefoil have all shown promise in cutting methane production. It can be cut by 12% simply by

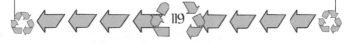

adding alfalfa, flax or hemp to a cow's usual feed. If every US dairy farmer were to do this, it would be the same as taking half a million cars off the road.

Scientists in New Zealand have worked out the genetic code of the microbes that cause methane production in ruminant animals like cows and sheep. It may lead to a vaccine that can be used to reduce the amount of methane the animals produce.

In Australia, 16% of greenhouse gas emissions come from agriculture and 66% of these are released as methane from farm livestock. Australian researchers have discovered that some sheep burp less than others. It may be possible to use these sheep to breed more low-methane sheep.

Reduce forest clearance

The destruction of forests is widespread and it causes global warming. Mature trees store a lot of carbon. The Amazon rainforest is one of the world's biggest carbon stores on land. When forests are cleared and burned, the carbon they contain is released into the atmosphere as carbon dioxide. Deforestation in Indonesia is now the world's third biggest emitter of carbon dioxide, with Brazil coming just behind in fourth position. Deforestation represents up to 75% of Brazil's greenhouse gas emissions.

forest facts

- 80% of the forests that covered the Earth have been damaged or destroyed – half of that in the past 30 years.
- About 20% of the world's oxygen is produced by the Amazon rainforest.
- Up to 90% of West Africa's coastal rainforests have disappeared since 1900.
- In South Asia, nearly 90% of the rainforests have been lost.
- Much of what remains of the world's rainforests is in the Amazon basin, where the Amazon Rainforest covers approximately 4 million square kilometres.
- Brazil has lost 90–95% of its Mata Atlântica forest.
- Madagascar has lost 90% of its eastern rainforests.

Capturing carbon

Fossil fuels could be made less damaging to the environment by stopping the carbon dioxide they produce from escaping into the atmosphere. Coal, the dirtiest of the fossil fuels, is the main focus of this work. There are two ways to do it. In coal-fired power stations, the carbon dioxide can be taken out of the coal before it's burned or after burning it.

To get the carbon dioxide out before burning the coal, powdered coal is cooked to change it into gas and dust. The gas is mostly hydrogen and carbon monoxide. The hydrogen is burned in the powerplant and the carbon monoxide is reacted with water to make more hydrogen and carbon dioxide, which is captured. To take out the carbon dioxide after burning, the gas that normally goes up the power station chimney is passed through 'scrubbers' that remove the carbon dioxide chemically.

Once the carbon dioxide has been captured, it has to be stored somewhere where it can't get out again. It can be pumped into underground oil and gas fields, where it will be trapped by the rock above it. This part of the system has already been used for decades. Carbon dioxide is routinely pumped down into underground rock to push out more oil and gas.

Getting rid of carbon dioxide like this is called carbon capture and storage (CCS). One of its drawbacks is that it needs a lot of energy. Up to 40% of a power station's energy could be needed to run the CCS system. And it's expensive. It could cost up to £1 billion to fit a CCS system to each power station. The first CCS powerplant was a small pilot plant opened in northern Germany in 2008 at the Vattenfall Schwarze Pumpe power station in Spremberg. It generates 30 megawatts of heat and 12 megawatts of electricity. If CCS can be proved to work here, it may be possible to use the hundreds of years of coal that are still under the ground without making Earth uninhabitable because of climate change.

How carbon capture and storage works

1. Mining of fuel
2. Coal- or gas-fired power station with CO_2 capture plant
3. CO_2 transport by pipeline
4. CO_2 injection
5. CO_2 storage sites

gas field

depleted oil and gas fields

CHAPTER EIGHT

WHAT CAN WE DO ABOUT IT?

PART 2:
RENEWABLE
ENERGY SOURCES

Unlike fossil fuels, which will not last forever, renewable energy sources will be there for as long as the Earth itself is habitable. Renewable energy sources include wind, wave, tidal, hydroelectricity, biomass, geothermal and solar. All forms of renewable energy together contribute about 13% of the energy used globally. Excluding large hydro power plants, renewables generate about 5% of global electricity.

Wind energy

Windmills have been used as a source of energy for grinding grain and powering machines since ancient times. The windmill was probably invented in Persia (present-day Iran) in the seventh century. They spread to, or were invented separately in, Europe in about the 12th century.

Today, electricity is generated from the wind by wind turbines, or aerogenerators, the modern equivalent of the ancient windmill. A turbine's blades, turned by the wind, drive a generator which produces electricity. Thousands of wind turbines are installed in the USA and thousands more in Europe. The average wind turbine generates enough electricity for about 300 homes.

Onshore and offshore – A common objection to wind turbines is that they spoil the appearance of beautiful countryside. One way to overcome this is to install the turbines offshore. Parts of the world with lots of windy coasts, such as the British Isles, are ideal for offshore wind farms. The wind blows stronger

and steadier offshore than over the land. The world's biggest offshore wind farm is off the coast of Denmark. Its 91 turbines are 30 km (18.6 miles) off the coast of Jutland. They came online in 2009, generating enough electricity for 200,000 homes. At the beginning of 2010, the British government announced plans for what will be the world's biggest offshore wind project. The aim is to generate a quarter of the UK's electricity from wind by 2020.

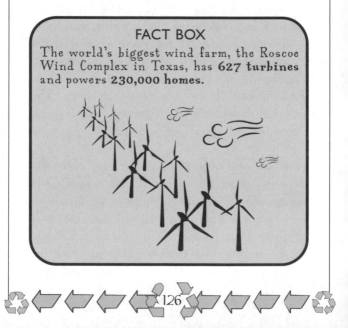

FACT BOX

The world's biggest wind farm, the Roscoe Wind Complex in Texas, has **627 turbines** and powers **230,000 homes**.

Wave energy

Waves are produced by wind blowing across the surface of the oceans and seas, and they carry a lot of energy. There have been attempts to develop wave energy for more than 100 years, but it is still the least used form of renewable energy. The devices currently in development use the up-and-down motion of the water's surface to drive a generator.

Salter's Duck – Researchers started looking at alternative ways to generate electricity in the 1970s. The first successful wave energy device was Salter's Duck. It was developed in 1974 by Professor Stephen Salter of the University of Edinburgh, Scotland. It sat in the water, nodding up and down. The nodding motion was used to drive a generator. It was a very efficient device. In experiments, it captured up to 90% of a wave's energy and changed about 90% of this into electricity. However, a full-size Salter's Duck was never tested in the sea. The research was done at a time when oil prices were rocketing. When oil became cheaper again a few years later, interest in wave energy waned and funding for the research was cut off.

Sea snakes

One common type of wave energy generator in use today looks like a big floating snake, 180 metres (590 feet) long and 4 metres (13.1 feet) across. As the waves wash past it, the 'snake' flexes, forcing hydraulic fluid (oil) through hydraulic motors, which drive generators. The electricity travels down a cable to the seabed, where several devices are connected together. A seabed cable carries the electricity to the shore. One of these machines can generate up to 750 kilowatts of electricity, or about enough to supply about 500 homes.

A 'sea snake', using wave energy to generate power

Tidal energy

While wave power generators use the action of waves, tidal power generators use the ebb and flow of the tides to generate electricity. Unlike waves, which move across the water's surface all the time, tides wash in and out just twice a day. At low tide and high tide, there is little or no water flowing in or out, so power generation falls to zero.

Where do the tides come from? – The tides are caused by the Moon. The Moon stays in orbit around Earth because of the force of gravity between them. This attracts water on Earth towards the Moon. A large bulge of water piles up on the Earth beneath the Moon. A smaller bulge of water sits on the opposite side of the planet. As the Earth turns, the bulges of water move around the Earth, following the Moon. The sea level rises as the Moon passes overhead and again just over 12 hours later.

Using the tides – One way to use the tides as a source of energy is the tidal barrage. A tidal barrage is a dam built across a river estuary. The tide comes in through gaps in the barrage, where the flow of water drives turbines. When the tide turns, the water flows out and powers the turbines again.

A barrage isn't the only way to use tidal energy. Turbines can be placed directly in the sea. Doing it this way is less expensive than building a barrage and it is less of a hindrance to ships and leisure boats.

Hydroelectricity

The most common way to produce electricity from water is a hydroelectric power plant. A dam is built across a river. where water piles up behind it, forming a reservoir. The water flows down a channel in the dam to turbines, which power generators. The higher the water level behind the dam, the faster the water is travelling when it hits the turbines.

La Rance Tidal Powerplant

The world's first electricity generating tidal powerplant opened in France in 1966. It is built across the Rance River in Brittany.

The barrage consists of a dam 750 metres (2,460 feet) long, containing 24 turbo-generators, each capable of generating 10 megawatts of electric power. At full power, generating 240 megawatts, the barrage can power 4% of the homes in Brittany.

Why at the Rance? The barrage was built at the Rance River, because of its big tidal range. The tidal range is the difference in height between the water levels at high tide and low tide. A big tidal range produces fast-flowing water that can generate more electricity. The tidal range at the Rance averages 8 metres (26 feet), but can be as much as 13.5 metres (44 feet).

FACT BOX

About **16%** of all the world's electricity is generated by large hydroelectric power plants. Norway is the world leader, as more than **98%** of Norway's electricity comes from hydroelectric power plants.

Biomass

Biomass is plant material, such as wood or grass, and animal waste. Biomass is the oldest source of energy on Earth. When our distant ancestors discovered the secret of making fire, perhaps as long ago as 800,000 years before now, they burned biomass in the form of wood for cooking and heat. Today, half of the world's population still relies on wood as their main source of energy.

Biomass is becoming popular again, but not to burn on open fires. Burning biomass can provide the heat that power stations use to make the steam that drives their turbines. Biomass power stations have been operating in a small way for decades, but now they're on the increase.

Britain is building the world's biggest biomass power station. The plant, in Wales, will produce 350 megawatts by burning wood chips from sustainable forests. It is expected to produce 50–80% less carbon dioxide emissions than a gas or coal-fired power station.

Recycling carbon – Biomass is not free of harmful emissions. It contains carbon. When it is burned, the carbon is released into the atmosphere as carbon dioxide. However, unlike fossil fuels, which release billions of tonnes of carbon dioxide that has been under the ground for millions of years, the carbon released from biomass is carbon that the biomass absorbed from the atmosphere in the previous few months or years. Growing new biomass to use as fuel takes this carbon out of the atmosphere again. Biomass recycles today's carbon, whereas fossil fuels add extra carbon from the past to our atmosphere today.

Biofuels – Another way to use biomass is to convert it into fuel to burn in engines instead of petrol and diesel. When plants are heated, treated with chemicals or fermented, they break down into a variety of solids, liquids and gases that can be used as fuels. The worldwide production of biofuels amounted to more than 53 billion litres in 2007. This represented about 4% of the 1.3 trillion litres of petrol used globally in that year. Brazil is a world leader in biofuel. Its bio-ethanol programme began 30 years ago and now the petrol sold in Brazilian fuel stations contains 20% ethanol. Brazil has also opened the world's first ethanol-powered power station.

Fuel vs food – Like any other crop, biomass needs a large area of land to grow on. If land that previously grew food crops is changed to growing energy crops, perhaps because they fetch a higher price, then food supply can suffer. Since 2006, tens of thousands of farmers have switched from food crops to biofuel crops. The land turned over to biofuel crops between 2006 and 2008 in the USA alone would have grown enough grain to feed nearly 250 million people. The global rush to

grow biofuel crops is credited with causing dramatic rises in food prices, which has led to food riots in several Third World countries. So, it is important that agricultural waste products and crops that do not replace food crops are used for biofuel.

"It is very hard to imagine how we can see a world growing enough crops to produce renewable energy and, at the same time, meet the enormous increase in the demand for food."

Britain's chief scientist,
Professor John Beddington.

Fuel from slime – An alternative source of biofuel that does not threaten food supply is algae – green slime. Algae contain oil, which can be converted into fuel. It's already been tried and it's very efficient. Experimental algae fuel schemes suggest that they can produce up to 30% more oil than the same area of traditional biofuel crops.

FACT BOX
Biofuels provide about **4%** of all the energy used in the USA.

Geothermal energy

In 1911, a new type of power station opened in Lardello, Italy. It didn't burn any fuel. It wasn't powered by wind, water or the Sun, and nuclear power hadn't been developed yet. It was the world's first geothermal power station.

Geothermal energy is heat from inside the Earth. Deep inside the Earth, the temperature is as high as the surface of the Sun. It's caused by radioactive decay. Luckily for us, the Earth's surface is a lot cooler. For every 100 metres (330 feet) you go down below the ground, the temperature rises by about 3°C (5.4°F). The deepest mines are so hot that they have to be cooled for the miners.

The most geothermal energy within easy reach of the Earth's surface is located in volcanically active regions, mainly around the 'ring of fire', the rim of the Pacific Ocean. The Romans used geothermal energy to heat public baths. The city of Bath in England was named after the naturally hot Roman baths there.

Today, geothermal power stations use this underground heat to make steam to power turbogenerators. The USA generates more electricity from geothermal energy than any other country. There are 34 geothermal power stations in California, 15 in Nevada and one each in Hawaii, Montana and Utah.

Harnessing geothermal energy

1. A deep production well is dug to an underground steam reservoir.

2. The pressurised steam is released and piped to a power plant, where its force turns a turbine.

3. The turbine powers a generator that converts the rotational energy into electricity.

4. The steam is condensed into the reservoir.

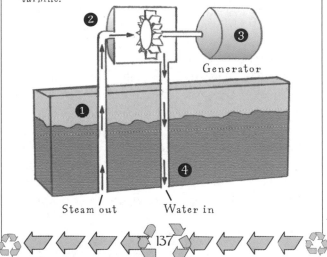

Generator

Steam out   Water in

Heat pumps – There is another way to use geothermal energy. A geothermal heat pump takes heat from the ground just a few metres down and uses it to heat buildings or to run air conditioning systems that cool buildings. More than 2 million of these ground-source heat pumps are used in 30 countries for heating or cooling.

Solar energy

Solar energy is energy from sunlight. It can be used in two ways. The sunlight can be changed directly into electricity by solar cells. This is called solar PV (photovoltaic). Alternatively, the heat energy in sunlight can be used for heating water, called solar thermal.

Solar PV – The first solar cell was invented by Charles Fritts as long ago as 1883. The modern silicon solar cell was invented by Russell Ohl in 1941. Then in 1954, Gerald Pearson, Calvin Fuller and Daryl Chapin developed a more efficient solar cell. With the advent of the Space Age, solar cells were developed for use on satellites. Today, there are solar powered traffic signs, battery chargers, water pumps, swimming pool heaters and even radio stations.

Some householders and businesses are putting solar panels on their roofs to reduce their electricity bills. Any surplus electricity produced is sold to the grid. About 1.5 million homes worldwide are generating electricity from sunlight and feeding it into the electricity grid.

Solar thermal – Solar thermal systems use solar energy to heat water in homes and to generate electricity in commercial power plants. Solar-heated water can be used directly in homes. Solar cookers and ovens are used in parts of the Third World, because they require no fuel. Nearly 50 million households worldwide use solar water heaters. In solar power stations, solar energy converts water into steam to run turbogenerators.

FACT BOX

The amount of sunlight that falls on Earth in **one hour** is enough to meet the world's energy needs for **a year**.

Experimental solar thermal electricity generating plants were built in the USA and Spain in the 1980s. The world's biggest solar thermal power plant is SEGS (Solar Electricity Generating Systems) in California's Mojave Desert. It has nine separate solar power plants generating a total of 350 megawatts – enough to supply more than 230,000 homes. This is a huge amount, but a solar thermal power plant built on just 1% of the Sahara Desert would generate the entire world's electricity needs.

Nevada Solar One

Nevada Solar One is a solar-powered electricity generating plant near Boulder City in the US state of Nevada. It generates 64 megawatts of electricity, which is enough to supply 14,000 homes.

A field of mirrors – Nevada Solar One is one of the world's biggest concentrating solar power plants. It started operating in 2007, less than 18 months after construction work began. It consists of 182,400 parabolic mirrors covering an area of 357,200 square metres (3.8 million square feet). The mirrors reflect sunlight onto

18,240 tubes, called receivers, full of fluid. The curved shape of the mirrors concentrates and multiplies the Sun's heating effect.

Making steam – The fluid, now heated to 390°C (735°F), is piped through water tanks, where the high temperature converts the water to steam. The steam drives the power plant's turbines. It is then condensed (changed back to water) and used again. Every two minutes, the mirrors rotate a fraction to track the Sun's path across the sky.

Temperature trouble – Nevada Solar One's receiver tubes heat up during the day and cool down at night. When different materials heat up and cool down, they expand and contract at different rates. If this happened at Solar One, it could crack the receiver tubes or cause leaks. To solve this problem, the glass manufacturer, Schott, developed a new type of glass that expands and contracts at the same rate as the metal parts.

A power plant like Nevada Solar One, but covering a much bigger area of 160 by 160 km (100 by 100 miles), would be able to generate all the USA's electricity needs.

FACT BOX

The carbon dioxide saved by Nevada Solar One is equivalent to taking **19,000 cars** off the road.

Electric cars

In the 1890s, the world's fastest cars were electric. However, they were rapidly overtaken by petrol-engine cars and fell into decline. Now, with concerns about global warming, it looks like electric cars are set to make a comeback.

Battery-powered electric cars emit no carbon dioxide. However, much of the electricity used to recharge their batteries is generated in fossil fuel power stations, so they could be said to be merely moving greenhouse emissions from the car to the power station. Another disadvantage is that it takes far longer to recharge an electric car's battery than to fill a tank with petrol.

Hybrid cars – One answer is the hybrid car. It has a petrol engine and an electric motor. The electric motor powers the car until its battery output runs low or more acceleration or speed is needed, when the petrol engine starts and takes over. The petrol engine also charges the battery. Ferdinand Porsche built the first petrol-electric hybrid car in 1900, but hybrid cars did not become widely available until Toyota produced the Prius in 1997.

Fuel cells – Fuel cells offer a cleaner way to power cars. They use a chemical reaction between hydrogen (or a chemical rich in hydrogen) and oxygen from the air to produce electricity and water vapour. As long as they are supplied with hydrogen, they carry on producing electricity. The first fuel cell was built in 1838 by Welsh scientist Sir William Robert Grove, based on work by the German scientist Christian Friedrich Schönbein the previous year. The fuel cell came into its own during the Space Race, when NASA developed fuel cells to power the two-man Gemini spacecraft. Fuel cells also powered the Apollo command module and the Space Shuttle. Fuel cell cars have been developed by several large manufacturers and could go on sale to the public during the 2010s. Cars that burn hydrogen in the normal way have also been developed.

Nuclear energy

Nuclear energy offers a cleaner alternative to fossil fuels for generating electricity. The story of nuclear electricity began in 1917 when Ernest Rutherford succeeded in splitting the atom. Splitting an atom is also called nuclear fission.

Then in 1934, Enrico Fermi split a uranium atom in two by firing neutrons at it. As the uranium nucleus broke apart, it gave out a burst of energy and more neutrons.

Scientists realised that these neutrons could be used to split more uranium atoms and produce a self-sustaining process – a process that would carry on all by itself. This is called a chain reaction. Further research resulted in the world's first man-made nuclear reactor. It was called Chicago Pile-1 and it achieved a self-sustaining nuclear chain reaction on December 2, 1942.

Nuclear electricity – A nuclear chain reaction produces more than enough heat energy to boil water and make steam. The steam can drive turbines and power electricity generators. In 1951, an experimental reactor called EBR-1, at Arco, Idaho, was the first nuclear reactor to produce electricity. Three years later, a small prototype nuclear reactor in the Russian city of Obninsk was the first nuclear power plant to supply electricity to the public power grid.

The world's first commercial nuclear power station, Calder Hall in England, was opened by Queen Elizabeth II in 1956. The age of nuclear power had arrived. Today, about 15% of the world's electricity is generated by nuclear reactors.

FACT BOX

A tiny **7-gram pellet of uranium fuel** the size of your fingertip generates the same amount of electricity as burning **3.5 barrels of oil** (557 litres or 147 US gallons), **481 cubic metres** (17,000 cubic feet) of natural gas or **807 kg** (1,780 pounds) of coal.

In most countries, few nuclear power stations were built from the mid-1980s onwards, because of worries about accidents, terrorist attacks and waste disposal problems. France was one of the few countries that forged ahead with nuclear power. Today, nuclear power stations meet 76% of France's electricity needs – a higher percentage than in any other country.

Today, the need to reduce carbon dioxide emissions is leading governments to look again at nuclear power. About 50 new nuclear reactors are planned for construction in the next few years.

Nuclear waste – Nuclear reactors produce radioactive waste. Scientists and engineers worked out how to dispose of it safely decades ago, but successive governments have failed to take the decisions needed to deal with it. For now, the waste is stored above ground. About 12,000 tonnes of high-level nuclear waste, the most dangerous, is produced every year. It's very hot, so it has to be kept in secure ponds, covered with water, for decades until it cools down.

In future, radioactive waste from nuclear reactors is likely to be buried deep underground in stable rock. But first it will have to be processed so that the radioactivity can't leak out. One method is called vitrification. The waste is mixed with sugar and glass and heated until it melts. When it cools and solidifies, the glass locks in the radioactivity. The glass is packed in steel cylinders, which can then be stored at a secure site.

Nuclear accidents

The great fear associated with nuclear power today is that an accident could release radioactive material. Unlike an accident with fossil fuels, radiation from nuclear fuel is invisible and it can affect unborn generations by damaging DNA. Since the nuclear age began in the 1940s, there have been five serious nuclear accidents:

- A fire at the Windscale nuclear plant, England (1957)
- An explosion at the Kyshtym nuclear waste facility, Soviet Union (1957)
- An explosion at the SL-1 military nuclear reactor, USA (1961)
- A partial melt-down at the Three Mile Island nuclear power station, USA (1979)
- An explosion at the Chernobyl nuclear power plant, Soviet Union (1986)

Fire at Windscale – In the late 1940s, a production plant for making plutonium for nuclear weapons was built on a remote stretch of coastline, called Windscale, in northwest England. Each of its two nuclear reactors, called Pile No.1 and Pile No. 2, consisted of more than 2,000 tonnes of graphite surrounded by a concrete shield. Channels in the graphite held the fuel rods. The reactors produced a great deal of heat. They were cooled by air blowing through them and then up two 120-metre (394-feet) tall chimneys. On October 10,

1957, workers noticed the temperature in Pile No. 1 was rising. Blowing more air through the pile failed to cool it. Radiation detectors were also registering a release of radioactive particles. The workers realised that something was terribly wrong. When they looked inside the pile, it was glowing red hot. Soon afterwards, it burst into flames.

By midnight, a radioactive cloud was drifting away from the plant to the northeast. Workers tried to extinguish the fire with carbon dioxide, but this failed. Water proved to be more successful. The fire was out by noon the following day.

After the fire, local farms were not allowed to sell milk because of radioactive contamination. Studies estimated that radioactive fall-out from the accident may have caused about 100 deaths.

Kyshtym – The Windscale fire was thought to be the first nuclear accident, but unknown to the world at that time, there had already been an even worse accident.

In the early 1950s, the Soviet Union built a store for nuclear waste near the Russian town of Kyshtym. A month before the Windscale fire, the cooling system for some of the waste tanks failed and the temperature of the waste started rising. The soaring temperature caused an explosion powerful enough to hurl the tank lid, weighing about 150 tonnes, into the air. It crashed to the ground 30 metres (98 ft) away.

The blast was as powerful as 70 tonnes of high explosive. Radioactive fall-out contaminated 800 square kilometres (309 square miles) of land.

Ten thousand people were evacuated from the area, but the evacuations did not begin until a week after the accident. Evacuated villages were burned and the top layer of soil was scraped away. Approximately 200 deaths are thought to have been caused by the accident, which was kept secret until details leaked to the West in the 1970s.

SL-1 – Stationary Low-power reactor number 1, or SL-1, was an experimental military nuclear reactor in Idaho, USA. On January 3, 1961, it was being started by pulling out its single control rod. Control rods soak up neutrons flying about inside the reactor and stop them from splitting atoms. Pushing the control rods into a reactor slows or stops the chain reaction. Pulling the control rods out lets the chain reaction speed up and the reactor becomes hotter.

SL-1 had just one control rod. On this occasion it was pulled out too far and too fast. In just 4 milliseconds, the reactor's temperature soared so high that water surrounding it instantly vaporised and exploded. The whole reactor jumped 3 metres (10 ft) in the air. Three workers died.

The SL-1 design was abandoned after the accident and all later reactors were designed so that removing one control rod could not cause the same sort of accident.

Chernobyl – The world's worst nuclear accident up to now happened on April 26, 1986, in Ukraine. Workers at the Chernobyl nuclear power plant were carrying out a test that involved shutting down reactor number four's cooling system. As the reactor started to heat up, the control rods were pushed into the core. Normally, pushing the control rods into the reactor should have mopped up neutrons and brought the reactor under control, but that's not what happened that day at Chernobyl.

The core was already so hot that some of the control rods broke up and others got stuck. The reactor temperature continued rising. Eventually, the reactor casing burst, tearing off its 2,000-tonne lid. A few seconds later, the fuel exploded.

Radioactive fuel was blasted 1,200 metres (nearly 4,000 ft) into the air. Then graphite in the core burst into flames. It took ten days to put the fire out. Meanwhile, 5,000 tonnes of sand, clay and other materials were dumped on the reactor from helicopters. Radiation levels were so high that many of the workers who tried to deal with the accident received lethal doses within minutes and died soon afterwards.

The West only learned of the accident when radiation detectors at a Swedish nuclear power plant sounded an alarm. Radiation from the accident was later detected as far away as the USA and Japan. A third of a million people had to be evacuated from the area around the reactor. A concrete cover, or sarcophagus, was quickly built to entomb the reactor's radioactive ruins. About 95% of the original fuel is still inside it.

FACT BOX

The Chernobyl accident released **400 times** the amount of radiation given out by the nuclear bomb dropped on the Japanese city of Hiroshima in 1945.

What can you do?

Factors like how we generate electricity or make fuels are controlled by governments, but individual people can make a difference too. In many developed countries, including the UK, up to 40% of the carbon dioxide emitted is due to the things that individual people do, so individuals can reduce these carbon dioxide emissions. Here's what you can do:

- Use energy-saving light-bulbs

- Turn computers and TV sets off instead of leaving them on standby

- Travel less by car

- Take fewer flights

- Insulate your home better

- Turn your central heating or air conditioning down

- Practice carbon offsetting

- Recycle as much rubbish as possible

- Use solar panels, a wind turbine, a solar water heater or 'green' grid electricity generated from environmentally friendly sources.

New bulbs

European Union countries started phasing out incandescent light bulbs in 2009. These bulbs waste a lot of energy because of the way they work. They heat up a thin wire filament until it glows. A lot of the electrical energy they use is changed to heat instead of light. A different type of bulb is much more efficient.

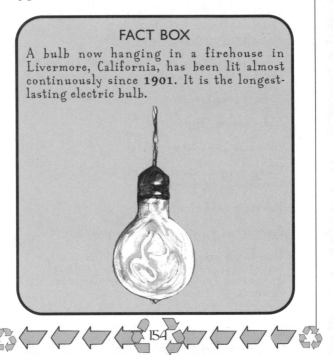

FACT BOX

A bulb now hanging in a firehouse in Livermore, California, has been lit almost continuously since **1901**. It is the longest-lasting electric bulb.

Saving energy

Europe is switching from incandescent bulbs to energy-saving compact fluorescent lamps (CFLs). These work like fluorescent tubes. Electricity makes gas inside the lamp produce invisible ultraviolet light and then the chemical coating inside the lamp changes this into white light.

Energy-saving bulbs use between a fifth and a third of the energy used by incandescent bulbs. The switch-over to energy-saving light bulbs will save Europe the electricity normally used by 11 million homes, cutting carbon dioxide emissions by about 15 million tonnes per year.

FACT BOX

The energy-saving compact fluorescent lamp was invented by **Ed Hammer** at General Electric in 1976.

CHAPTER NINE

FUTURE FIXES

Scientists have suggested a variety of ways to reduce global warming. They range from buildings that use energy more efficiently to fitting the Earth with sunshades!

Energy efficient buildings

Old buildings lose a lot of heat energy through their roofs and because of draughts. Many of them are heated by old, inefficient water boilers. Simply insulating these buildings better, dealing with draughts and replacing old boilers with new energy-saving boilers can save several tonnes of carbon dioxide emissions per house per year... and also reduce

the building's heating bills. Some buildings are designed from scratch to be energy efficient, so that they need minimal heating in winter and minimal cooling in summer. They may have solar panels or solar water heaters on the roof. If they are located in the northern hemisphere, their south-facing windows may be bigger to capture more solar energy, while the north-facing windows are smaller to lose less heat. The windows themselves may be made from more thermally efficient glass that lets less heat escape.

They may have a wind turbine to generate electricity, although the turbulent air-flow around buildings in cities often makes cities poor places to use wind turbines. More buildings today have ground-source heat pumps to take heat from the ground and use it for warmth. More home-owners are installing underground tanks for storing rainwater. Using this for watering gardens and washing the car saves drinking water, which requires energy to produce.

The Pearl River Tower

Skyscrapers could be a lot more energy efficient. The Pearl River Tower in China shows what is possible. This is a 'green' skyscraper with built-in wind turbines and solar panels to reduce its electricity needs from the grid.

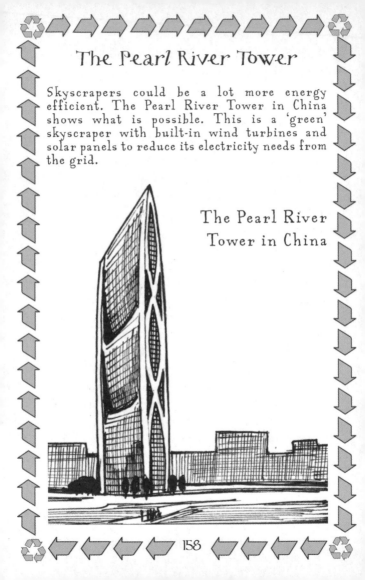

The Pearl River Tower in China

Artificial trees

Trees soak up carbon dioxide, so one idea is to make thousands of artificial trees to take even more carbon dioxide out of the atmosphere. The trees would contain a resin that absorbs more carbon dioxide than a real tree. Experimental artificial trees have already been built and tested. Just one of these big industrial-scale artificial trees could remove more than 80,000 tonnes of carbon dioxide from the atmosphere every year. The gas is then extracted from the tree, by watering the resin, and stored.

Making electricity from roads!

Israeli scientists have found a way to generate electricity from roads. Some materials produce electricity when they are squeezed. They're called piezoelectric materials. When materials like this were built into a road surface, every time a car travelled along the road, its weight compressed the piezoelectric material and produced electricity.

159

Ironing the oceans

Plants need tiny amounts of iron for photosynthesis (making food by using energy from sunlight). Vast tracts of the world's oceans are crystal clear because there is not enough iron dissolved in the water to support the growth of algae. Huge amounts of algae could be made to grow in the oceans by dissolving iron in the water. Growing algae would extract carbon dioxide from the atmosphere and then sink, carrying the carbon dioxide with it. Every tonne of iron ore added to seawater would remove up to 100,000 tonnes of carbon dioxide from the atmosphere.

When Mount Pinatubo erupted in the Philippines in 1991, it dumped about 40,000 tonnes of iron dust in the oceans. The growth in algae this triggered caused a measurable reduction in atmospheric carbon dioxide and a corresponding increase in oxygen. Scientists have also performed experiments, seeding small areas of ocean with iron and studying the results. They confirmed that adding iron to the ocean would indeed produce algal growth that would absorb carbon dioxide.

Dusting the atmosphere

When a large volcano erupts, the dust it throws up into the atmosphere reduces the amount of solar energy that reaches the ground. The eruption of Mount Pinatubo in 1991 reduced global temperatures by about 0.3°C (0.54°F). So, one idea is to spread millions of tonnes of sulphate particles in the stratosphere from balloons. This would mimic a huge volcanic eruption and reduce the amount of solar energy reaching the Earth's surface, which should cool the planet. However, it would be very expensive and meteorologists say it could reduce rainfall around the Mediterranean and Middle East. Tens of thousands of tonnes of sulphates would have to be added to the atmosphere every month.

Of course, there's no reason why an artificial method has to mimic a volcanic eruption so closely. There may be other chemicals that would work even better. Professor David Keith of the University of Calgary is looking for more efficient chemicals for the job.

Masdar

In the future, whole cities could be designed from scratch to use as little energy as possible. One of these energy efficient cities is already being built. It's called Masdar.

Masdar is the world's first car-free, zero-carbon-dioxide, zero-waste city. It's being built on a six million square metres (2.3 square miles) site in Abu Dhabi, and is due to be completed by 2016. Up to 90,000 people will live and work there, but there will be no cars. Private cars will be replaced by zero-carbon public transport. Masdar's designers are aiming for:

- **100% renewable energy**
- **Carbon neutral city**
- **Zero waste**
- **The world's greenest commercial buildings**

The planned Masdar City
Headquarters in Abu Dhabi

Electricity

Electricity for the city will be provided by solar power plants and wind farms. In addition, there will be solar panels on roof-tops. The world's largest hydrogen power plant is planned and there may be a geothermal power plant too. Solar-powered low energy LED street lights will illuminate the city.

Water

Masdar is located near the Persian Gulf coast of Abu Dhabi, so fresh water will be provided by a solar-powered desalination plant. It will make fresh water by taking salt out of seawater. Up to 80% of the city's water will be recycled, probably several times. When it can't be recycled for human use any more, it will be used to water crops.

Waste

Even the city's waste won't be wasted. Biodegradable waste (waste that breaks down naturally) will be used to make fertiliser and compost. Any remaining waste will be burned to provide more energy.

Transport

The city is being designed so that as many journeys as possible can be done on foot. Longer journeys will be made by using a fleet of 3,000 automated electric taxis and an electric light rail system. A high-speed rail link will connect Masdar to surrounding cities. No-one will be more than 200 metres (656 feet) from a transport link.

Nuclear fusion

Nuclear fission, the process used in nuclear power reactors today has some serious drawbacks. Although it doesn't produce the greenhouse gases that fossil fuels give rise to, the radioactive fuel is highly dangerous, as is the radioactive waste it creates. There is a better alternative, called nuclear fusion.

When very light atomic nuclei are slammed together hard enough, they stick together, or fuse, and give out energy. This is how the Sun works. At its core, the huge pressure and a temperature of 15 million °C (27 million °F) are enough to fuse hydrogen nuclei to form helium and give out the energy that makes the Sun shine.

The Sun has been doing this for the past 4.5 billion years. Every second, 4 million tonnes of the Sun disappears, changed into energy by nuclear fusion.

Scientists are trying to produce nuclear fusion on Earth. Instead of dangerous, expensive uranium, a fusion reactor would use a mixture

of two types of hydrogen called deuterium and tritium as a fuel. Ordinary hydrogen has one proton in its nucleus. Deuterium has one proton in its nucleus, too, but it also has a neutron, making it heavier than ordinary hydrogen. Tritium has a proton and two neutrons. Deuterium is found in the oceans and tritium is made in nuclear reactors.

Recreating the Sun on Earth is, to say the least, difficult. The immense pressure at the centre of the Sun cannot be produced on Earth, so to make up for this an Earth-bound fusion reactor has to work at a far higher temperature than the centre of the Sun – at least 100 million °C (180 million °F). The problem with this is that fuel at such a high temperature would melt through a container made of any known material. One answer is to surround the fuel with a magnetic field that holds it away from the walls of the reactor.

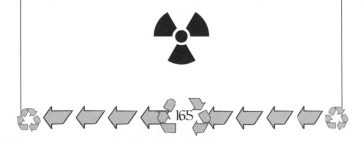

JET power

The Joint European Torus (JET) is an experimental nuclear fusion reactor. It was built in Culham, England, between 1977 and 1983. In 1991, it achieved the first ever controlled release of fusion power. In 1997, it achieved another world first. It generated 16 megawatts of fusion power. Unfortunately, 24 megawatts of power had to be pumped in to get it to work. And it only works for less than a second at a time.

The next step is to build a bigger, more powerful and more efficient reactor. This will be ITER (the International Thermonuclear Experimental Reactor). It is being built in Cadarache, in the south of France. It should be completed by 2033. ITER is designed to produce up to 500 megawatts of power and to work for several minutes at a time. Then the first nuclear fusion power plant will be built. This will be called DEMO. DEMO should be able to produce at least 2,000 megawatts of power continuously.

Both JET and ITER are a type of fusion reactor design called a Tokamak that was invented in the 1950s in Russia. The fuel is held inside a doughnut-shaped cavity. More than 30 tokamaks have been built since the 1950s.

Laser research

The tokamak isn't the only way to produce nuclear fusion. A different line of research in the USA concentrates on the use of lasers. A powerful laser pulse is fired at a small amount of fuel, compressing the fuel until it is dense enough and hot enough for fusion to occur. The National Ignition Facility has been built at the Lawrence Livermore Laboratory in California to carry out this research. The facility was completed in 2009. Experiments will concentrate the power of 192 giant lasers on a pellet of hydrogen fuel smaller than a fingertip in an attempt to create nuclear fusion.

CHAPTER TEN

WHAT ARE GOVERNMENTS DOING?

Individual people can make their own small contributions to reducing global warming. To make the really big cuts in carbon emissions that scientists say are needed, governments have to get together, make international agreements and then stick to them. Governments have been meeting to discuss climate change since the 1970s.

Stockholm Conference

The 1972 UN Conference on the Human Environment, better known as the Stockholm Conference, was the first major United Nations conference on the environment. It was attended

by representatives from 113 countries, 19 inter-governmental agencies and more than 400 other organisations. One of the main talking points was the damage being done to the ozone layer of the atmosphere by chemicals called chlorofluorocarbons (CFCs). At that time, CFCs were used in fridges and aerosol spray cans. Global warming was barely touched upon.

Rio Earth Summit

The UN Conference on Environment and Development, also known as the Rio Earth Summit, was held in Rio de Janeiro in 1992. It was attended by representatives of 172 governments and 2,400 other organisations. Another 17,000 people attended a Global Forum that was held alongside the conference.

Amongst other things, the conference discussed alternatives to fossil fuels, which were by then being linked to global warming. The growing scarcity of water and the need to use public transport more to reduce vehicle emissions were also discussed. The conference also established the UN Framework Convention on Climate Change UNFCCC) –

a treaty between governments to enable them to exchange information about greenhouse gas emissions and co-operate in developing ways to deal with climate change.

The Rio Earth Summit didn't commit governments to any legally binding limits on greenhouse gas emissions, but it did allow for future updates, called protocols, where these limits could be agreed. The most famous of these is the 1997 Kyoto Protocol.

The Kyoto Protocol

The Kyoto Protocol was the first international, legally binding agreement on climate change. In 1997, 37 industrialised nations agreed to cut their emissions by 5.2% (from their 1990 levels) by 2012. The USA, the world's biggest polluter at that time, signed up to the agreement under President Clinton, but withdrew from it when President George W. Bush was elected. The agreement finally became law in 2005 after Russia ratified it. By the end of 2009, 186 countries and the European Union had signed up to the Kyoto Protocol.

"I told the world I thought that Kyoto was a lousy deal for America"

US President George W. Bush.

Different targets were set for different countries. The European Union as a whole had to cut its emissions by 8%. Japan's target was 6%. Some countries were allowed to increase their emissions. Iceland was allowed to increase its emissions by 10%. Surprisingly, Australia, one of the worst polluters, was allowed to increase its emissions by 8%.

Countries had several ways to meet their commitments under the agreement. If a country's carbon emissions were higher than they were allowed to emit, they could buy carbon credits from other countries. The EU has the biggest carbon trading scheme, called the EU ETS. Countries could also earn carbon credits by funding climate-friendly projects in other countries.

APRIL
22
Earth Day!

Critics of Kyoto say that it limited greenhouse gas emissions from wealthy countries, but applied no limits on developing countries. One of the quirks of the agreement was that China, the world's biggest carbon dioxide emitter, was not required to reduce its emissions, because it was not responsible for the grave situation the world finds itself in today. Despite this historic agreement between so many countries to reduce carbon dioxide emissions, the emissions have actually increased since then.

How much do we have to do to get out of trouble?

A scientific meeting called "Avoiding Dangerous Climate Change" was held in Britain in 2005. Two hundred scientists from 30 countries discussed the problem. Some of the scientists suggested that the worst effects of climate change could be prevented if the rise in global temperature could be kept to less than 2°C (3.6°F), although other scientists at the meeting disagreed with this. A meeting of the G8 group of industrialised countries in

July 2009 agreed to make cuts in their carbon emissions to limit the rise in global temperature to 2°C (3.6°F). To achieve this, they will have to cut emissions by 80% by 2050 and other countries will have to cut their emissions by 50%.

Copenhagen Climate Conference

In December, 2009, 45,000 people including 115 world leaders met in the Danish capital to make a new agreement to take effect from the end of the Kyoto agreement in 2012. The main aims were to agree on a reduction in greenhouse gas emissions and increase financial help for poor countries to let them deal with the effects of climate change.

So, how did they do? Sadly, the conference was a failure. At the last minute, five countries (USA, China, India, Brazil and South Africa) produced a weak agreement that disappointed almost everyone. They agreed that it would be a good idea to keep temperature rise to no more than 2°C (3.6°F), but they didn't decide on the reductions in emissions needed to make

it happen. And the earlier deal to cut emissions by 80% by 2050 was dropped. This was a great disappointment to poor countries, who wanted all the countries at the conference to sign a legal deal to reduce their emissions by whatever amount was needed to keep global temperature rise to 1.5°C (2.7°F) or less.

Taking advice

Governments take decisions about global warming based on advice from scientists. But which scientists do they listen to? And how do they keep up with the thousands of scientific papers about global warming and climate change that are published every year? The answer is the IPCC. The IPCC is the Intergovernmental Panel on Climate Change. It was set up in 1988 by the United Nations Environment Program and the World Meteorological Organisation to study all the climate research carried out by scientists all over the world. Every six years, the IPCC publishes a report summarising it all. The last report was published in 2007.

The IPCC's reports

The first report in 1990 said that greenhouse gases produced by human activities are increasing. It also predicted that the world will warm more in the next 100 years than in the past 10,000 years, and that the sea level could rise by up to 65 cm (22 in).

The second report in 1995 found that greenhouse gases in the atmosphere are continuing to increase and that human activities do appear to be changing the climate.

The third report in 2001 predicted that the average global surface temperature could increase by up to 5.8°C (10.4°F) between 1990 and 2100.

By the time the fourth report was written in 2007, scientists were able to compare their 2001 predictions with what actually happened. The temperature was predicted to rise by up to 0.35°C (0.63°F). The actual rise was 0.33°C (0.59°F) – very close to the maximum prediction. Sea level had actually risen faster than the predictions.

The report now predicts a worst-case temperature rise of up to 6.4°C (11.5°F) by the end of this century. The oceans are warming not just at the surface but down to a depth of at least 3,000 m (9,840 ft). The report also stated that the amounts of carbon dioxide and methane in the atmosphere are far higher now than at any time in the past 650,000 years, and that human activities are the main cause.

Glossary

algae Simple green plants living in water and wet places, from single cells to large seaweeds.

Antarctic The region around the South Pole including the ice-covered continent, Antarctica, and the ocean surrounding it.

Arctic The icy region around the North Pole.

atmosphere The gases surrounding a planet or moon. The Earth's atmosphere is made of a mixture of gases called air.

biodegradeable Capable of being broken down by bacteria.

biofuel A solid, liquid or gas fuel made from recently-living biological material, such as plants.

carbon A non-metallic element widely found in the Earth's crust and in all plants and animals.

carbon capture and storage A method for trapping carbon dioxide, stopping it from being released into the atmosphere and locking it away permanently.

carbon dioxide A gas containing carbon and oxygen, given out by living organisms and produced when fossil fuels burn. Found in the atmosphere. A greenhouse gas.

carbon trading the buying and selling of carbon credits with the aim of reducing the amount of carbon dioxide released into the atmosphere.

chain reaction A series of nuclear reactions that carry on going. One very large atom of an element such as uranium or plutonium splits and gives out particles that split more atoms and so on.

climate The weather in one region averaged over a long time.

control rod A rod made of a material such as boron that absorbs neutrons. Control rods are pushed into a nuclear reactor to absorb neutrons and to slow or stop the chain reaction.

deuterium A form of hydrogen with a proton and neutron in its nucleus. Heavier than ordinary hydrogen, which has just a proton in its nucleus.

DNA DeoxyriboNucleic Acid. A long chain-like molecule found in living cells, containing the instructions for the growth and working of a plant or animal.

fall-out Radioactive dust that falls on the ground after a nuclear explosion.

forams Organisms, mainly microscopic, and found mainly in the sea. The fossilised skeletons of forams that lived up to 500 million years ago have been found.

fossil The remains or imprint of a plant or animal that lived in prehistoric times, now embedded in rock.

fossil fuel A fuel made from the remains of plants or animals that lived millions of years ago.

fuel A substance that can be used as a source of energy, usually by burning it.

fuel cell A device that converts fuel directly into electric current without burning it.

genome The complete genetic code of an organism.

global warming An increase in the temperature of the Earth's atmosphere.

graphite A form of carbon used in pencils and to control nuclear activity in some nuclear reactors.

greenhouse effect The process by which the atmosphere absorbs energy radiated from the Earth's surface as a result of solar heating.

greenhouse gas A gas that produces the greenhouse effect. The main greenhouse gases in Earth's atmosphere are methane, carbon dioxide, water vapour and nitrous oxide.

hydraulic fluid A liquid, usually oil, that transmits power in a hydraulic machine.

hydrogen The lightest and most abundant element in the Universe.

ice core A cylindrical section of ice taken out of a glacier or ice sheet to study the climate in the past.

jet stream One of several fast winds blowing around the world 13–20 km (8–12 miles) above the ground.

megawatt A unit of electrical power equal to 1,000 watts.

methane A colourless, odourless greenhouse gas that burns easily.

neutron An electrically neutral particle found in the nucleus of an atom.

nuclear fission A nuclear reaction in which a large nucleus splits in two and releases energy.

nuclear fusion A nuclear reaction in which two small atomic nuclei fuse together to form a bigger nucleus and release energy.

nucleus The particle or particles at the centre of an atom. Plural – nuclei.

permafrost Ground so cold that it is permanently frozen.

proton A positively charged particle found in the nucleus of an atom.

GLOSSARY

radiation Energy transmitted in the form of particles or rays.

radioactivity A property of some atoms by which they give out radiation.

renewable energy Energy obtained from natural sources, such as the Sun or wind, which is constantly produced and is not used up in the same way as coal or oil.

solar cell A device that changes sunlight into electricity.

solar energy Energy, usually heat or electricity, obtained from sunlight.

Space Race Competition between the USA and the Soviet Union to see which nation could make the greatest advances in spaceflight, especially landing astronauts on the Moon.

tidal barrage A structure built to extract energy from tides for generating electricity.

turbine A machine with a part that spins when a liquid or gas hits its vanes or blades. Turbines extract energy from moving liquids and gases for powering machines such as generators for producing electricity.

turbogenerator An electricity generator powered by a turbine.

uranium A heavy radioactive metallic element used as a fuel in nuclear reactors.

watt A unit of power that shows how fast energy is being converted from one form to another. 1 watt is equal to 1 joule of energy per second.

weather The temperature, wind, rain and other atmospheric conditions at a particular time and place.

Global warming timeline

1753 The Scottish chemist Joseph Black discovers carbon dioxide.

1776 Alessandro Volta discovers methane.

1793 Nitrous oxide is discovered by the English chemist Joseph Priestley.

1809 The world population is 1 billion.

1837 The German-Swiss chemist Christian Friedrich Schönbein discovers the scientific principle on which the fuel cell works.

1838 The first fuel cell is built by Welsh scientist Sir William Robert Grove.

1840 Christian Friedrich Schönbein discovers ozone.

1853 The first commercial oil well is drilled in Poland.

1859 Irish physicist John Tyndall discovers that some gases block infrared radiation and changes in gases in the atmosphere could cause global warming. The first oil well is drilled in the USA, at Titusville, Pennsylvania.

1860 The mean global temperature is about 13.6°C.

1870 The level of carbon dioxide in the atmosphere is about 290 parts per million.

1883 Charles Fritts invents the solar cell.

1896 Swedish chemist Svante Arrhenius is the first person to describe a man-made greenhouse effect caused by carbon dioxide produced by the burning of coal.

1900 Ferdinand Porsche builds the first petrol-electric hybrid car.

1911 The first geothermal power station opens in Lardello, Italy.

Global Warming Timeline

1920s The jet streams are discovered by Japanese meteorologist, Wasaburo Ooishi. The Texas and Persian Gulf oil fields open, beginning an era of cheap energy.

1924 The world population is 2 billion.

1930s The American pilot Wiley Post encounters a jet stream while making record-breaking high altitude flights. Milutin Milankovitch suggests that ice ages are caused by changes in the Earth's orbit.

1934 The Italian physicist Enrico Fermi achieves the first artificial nuclear fission, which leads to the development of nuclear power.

1938 British engineer Guy Callendar finds that the average temperature in several regions has increased over the previous century, and that carbon dioxide levels have risen by 10% in the same time. He wonders if the rise in carbon dioxide might have caused the rise in temperature.

1939 The German meteorologist H. Seilkopf invents the name jet streams for the fast, high-altitude winds that encircle the Earth.

1941 Russell Ohl invents the modern silicon solar cell.

1942 Physicists Enrico Fermi and Leo Szilard create the first man-made nuclear reactor, called Chicago Pile 1.

1951 The experimental nuclear reactor, EBR-1 in Arco, Idaho, is the first nuclear reactor to generate electricity.

1954 Gerald Pearson, Calvin Fuller and Daryl Chapin develop a more efficient solar cell. The Obninsk Nuclear Power Plant in Russia is the first to supply electricity to the grid.

1956 The world's first commercial nuclear power station, Calder Hall in Sellafield, England, opens. Nuclear fusion research using the Russian Tokamak reactor design begins.

1957 Windscale and Kyshtym nuclear accidents. Roger Revelle finds that carbon dioxide produced by human activities is not readily absorbed by the oceans.

1958 Charles Keeling measures carbon dioxide levels in the atmosphere and detects an annual rise in these levels.

1960 The mean global temperature is 13.9°C (57°F) and the level of carbon dioxide in the atmosphere is 315 parts per million. The world population is 3 billion.

1961 SL-1 nuclear accident

1963 Calculations suggest that water vapour in the atmosphere can make the climate very sensitive to changes in the level of carbon dioxide.

1965 A climate change conference is held in Boulder, Colorado.

1966 The Rance tidal barrage power plant opens in France.

1967 The International Global Atmospheric Research Program is set up, mainly to improve weather forecasting, but also to study climate. Syukuro Manabe and Richard Wetherald calculate that doubling the amount of carbon dioxide in the atmosphere would raise the global temperature by a couple of degrees.

1968 The astronauts of Apollo 8 photograph the Earth from lunar orbit, revealing the Earth as a fragile blue ball hanging in space. Climate studies suggest the possibility of a collapse of the Antarctic ice sheets, which would cause a catastrophic rise in sea levels.

1969 The Nimbus 3 satellite begins global atmospheric temperature measurements.

1970 The National Oceanic and Atmospheric Administration is set up in the USA to study the oceans and atmosphere, and to improve the understanding of climate change. The first Earth Day, a day designed to inspire a greater awareness of the Earth's environment is held. Aerosols (fine particles and droplets) produced by human activities are increasing rapidly, suggesting to some scientists that the cooling they produce could trigger an ice age.

1971 An SMIC (Study of Man's Impact on Climate) conference warns of the danger of rapid and serious global climate change caused by humans.

1972 Ice cores and other evidence suggest large shifts in climate in the past, especially about 11,000 years ago.

1973 An oil crisis encourages interest in alternative sources of energy.

1974 Salter's Duck, a wave energy device, is invented by Professor Stephen Salter. The world population is 4 billion.

1975 Syukuro Manabe and others create computer models that predict doubling the amount of carbon dioxide in the atmosphere will raise temperatures by several degrees.

1976 The energy-saving compact fluorescent lamp is invented by Ed Hammer at General Electric. Deep-sea cores reveal the effect of the 100,000-year Milankovitch orbital change on climate. John A. Eddy shows that the Sun is a variable star and that periods of cold climate coincided with times when solar activity was at a minimum.

1977 Most scientists agree that the main danger for the future is global warming, not global cooling.

1979 Three Mile Island nuclear accident. The World Climate Research Programme is launched to co-ordinate international climate research.

1983 Experiments with the Joint European Torus (JET) nuclear fusion reactor begin.

1985 Antarctic ice cores show that carbon dioxide and temperature went up and down together in past times.

1986 Chernobyl nuclear accident.

1987 The new warmest year on record. The Montreal Protocol agrees restrictions on the release of gases that harm the ozone layer of the atmosphere. The world population is 5 billion.

1988 The British Prime Minister, Margaret Thatcher, is the first major world leader to call for action on climate change. The Intergovernmental Panel on Climate change (IPCC) is established.

1989 The Global Climate Coalition is set up by a group of mainly US businesses to oppose actions to reduce greenhouse gas emissions.

1990 The IPCC reports that the world has been warming in the past and the warming seems likely to continue.

1991 Mount Pinatubo erupts, causing global cooling of 0.5°C (0.9°F).

1992 The Rio Earth Summit.

1993 Ice cores from Greenland suggest that great shifts in climate can occur in as little time as a decade.

1995 The new warmest year on record. The second IPCC report says that man-made greenhouse effects have been detected and that serious global warming is likely in the next century.

1997 Toyota introduces the Prius, the first mass market hybrid car. The Kyoto Protocol agrees targets for reducing greenhouse gas emissions.

1998 A super El Niño event makes 1998 the warmest year on record.

1999 The 1990s is declared the warmest decade in 1,000 years. The world population is 6 billion.

2001 US President George W. Bush refuses to sign up to the Kyoto Protocol because it will harm the US economy. The third IPCC report says that global warming unprecedented since the end of the last ice age is very likely with possibly severe effects. Warming in the oceans matches computer models of greenhouse effects.

2002 Global dimming due to air pollution has reduced global warming, but the dimming is decreasing.

2003 Tens of thousands of people die during a deadly summer heat wave in Europe.

2005 The Kyoto Protocol goes into effect, having been signed by major industrial nations except the USA and Australia. New Orleans is devastated by Hurricane Katrina. Cadarache, France, is chosen as the site for the new nuclear fusion research reactor, ITER (International Thermonuclear Experimental Reactor).

2006 *'An Inconvenient Truth'*, a film about former US Vice-President Al Gore's campaign to educate people about global warming, is released.

2007 The fourth IPCC report warns that serious effects of global warming are being detected. The Greenland and Antarctic ice sheets and Arctic Ocean sea-ice are found to be shrinking faster than expected. Australia finally signs up to the Kyoto Protocol. Former US Vice-President Al Gore and the IPCC jointly win the Nobel Peace Prize.

2008 More than 400 square kilometres (160 square miles) of the Wilkins Shelf breaks away from the Antarctic coast.

2009 The mean global temperature is 14.5°C (58.1°F) and the level of carbon dioxide in the atmosphere reaches 385 parts per million.

2010 The world population is 6.8 billion.

Index

Other titles in The Cherished Library

Ancient Egypt
A Very Peculiar History
The Art of Embalming:
Mummy Myth and Magic
With added Squishy Bits
Jim Pipe
ISBN: 978-1-906714-92-5

Brighton
A Very Peculiar History
With added Hove, actually
David Arscott
ISBN: 978-1-906714-89-5

Ireland
A Very Peculiar History
With NO added Blarney
Jim Pipe
ISBN: 978-1-905638-98-7

Rations
A Very Peculiar History
With NO added Butter
David Arscott
ISBN: 978-1-907184-25-3

London
A Very Peculiar History
With added Jellied Eels
Jim Pipe
ISBN: 978-1-907184-26-0

Vampires
A Very Peculiar History
With added Bite
Fiona Macdonald
ISBN: 978-1-907184-39-0

Scotland
A Very Peculiar History
With NO added Haggis
or Bagpipes
Fiona Macdonald

Vol. 1: From ancient times
to Robert the Bruce
ISBN: 978-1-906370-91-6

Vol. 2: From the Stewarts
to modern Scotland
ISBN: 978-1-906714-79-6

The Blitz
A Very Peculiar History
With NO added Doodlebugs
David Arscott
ISBN: 978-1-907184-18-5

Wales
A Very Peculiar History
With NO added Laverbread
Rupert Matthews
ISBN: 978-1-907184-19-2

The World Cup
A Very Peculiar History
With NO added Time
David Arscott
ISBN: 978-1-907184-38-3

Castles
A Very Peculiar History
With added dungeons
Jacqueline Morley
ISBN: 978-1-907184-48-2

Heroes, Gods and Monsters of
Ancient Greek Mythology
Michael Ford
ISBN: 978-1-906370-92-3

Heroes, Gods and Monsters of
Celtic Mythology
Fiona Macdonald
ISBN: 978-1-905638-97-0

The Triumph Of Charis

See the chariot at hand here of Love,
Wherein my lady rideth!
Each that draws is a swan or a dove,
And well the car Love guideth.
As she goes, all hearts do duty
Unto her beauty;
And, enamoured, do wish, so they might
But enjoy such a sight,
That they still were to run by her side,
Through swords, through seas, whither she would ride.

Do but look on her eyes, they do light
All that Love's world compriseth!
Do but look on her hair, it is bright
As Love's star when it riseth!
Do but mark, her forehead's smoother
Than words that soothe her!
And from her arched brows, such a grace
Sheds itself through the face,
As alone there triumphs to the life
All the gain, all the good, of the elements' strife.

Have you seen but a bright lily grow
Before rude hands have touched it?
Have you marked but the fall o' the snow
Before the soil hath smutched it?
Have you felt the wool of beaver?
Or swan's down ever?
Or have smelt o' the bud o' the brier?
Or the nard in the fire?
Or have tasted the bag of the bee?
O so white! O so soft! O so sweet is she!

Ben Jonson